KU-575-409

GOATS

CASSELL'S PET AND FANCY BOOKS

1. HAMSTERS by Percy Parslow
2. PONIES by Veronica Heath
3. RACING PIGEONS by Guy Barrett
4. FANCY MICE by R. S. Hutchings
5. BUDGERIGARS by W. Watmough
6. CAVIES by Alan Sole
7. BANTAMS by H. Easom Smith
8. GOATS by H. E. Jeffery
9. DONKEYS by Robin Borwick
10. CATS by Grace Pond and Elizabeth Towe
11. FANCY PIGEONS by W. Watmough
12. BEES AND BEEKEEPING by A. V. Pavord
13. RABBITS by H. Dyson
14. SIAMESE CATS by Elizabeth Towe
15. TROPICAL FISH AND AQUARIA by Leslie B. Katterns
16. CANARIES by George Lynch
17. EXOTIC BIRDS FOR CAGE AND AVIARY by Clive Roots
18. GARDEN PONDS AND INDOOR WATER GARDENS by Leslie B. Katterns
19. DOGS by Frank Jackson and W. Ronald Irving

British Saanen female goat, winner of Championship and Breed Championship Certificates at the Royal Show in five consecutive years and at the Royal Dairy Show in four consecutive years. Yield in first 365 days, officially recorded after:

1st kidding 4706 lb. at 3.54% butter fat
2nd kidding 4709 lb. at 3.6% butter fat
3rd kidding 4932 lb. at 3.38% butter fat

Owner and breeder: Miss. J. Mostyn Owen.

GOATS

by H. E. Jeffery

CASSELL · LONDON

CASSELL & COMPANY LTD.

an imprint of
Cassell & Collier Macmillan Publishers Ltd.
35 Red Lion Square, London WC1R 4SG
and at Sydney, Auckland, Toronto, Johannesburg

and an affiliate of The Macmillan Company Inc, New York

First edition 1970
Second edition 1975

I.S.B.N. 0 304 93417 8

Printed in Great Britain by
REDWOOD BURN LIMITED
Trowbridge & Esher.

CONTENTS

ACKNOWLEDGEMENTS

The author acknowledges with gratitude the co-operation of the British Goat Society, Mrs. M. E. Egerton and other members of that Society in the preparation of this book.

CHAPTER I
The Goat

The goat, genus *Capra*, is a member of the family *Bovidae* (*Artiodactyla Ungulates*) – cloven-hooved mammals which include cattle and sheep. Visually it is close to the sheep but distinguished from it by the skin covering being primarily hair rather than wool. The frequent presence of a beard and the odour of the male are other differences. There have in fact been instances of mating between a sheep and a goat, and vice versa, but no live progeny have been confirmed.

Attempts have been made to classify goats into several species, according to the shape of the horn, but this classification is confused.

The goat was one of the first animals to be domesticated. Of a size that can be controlled and handled readily, it produces flesh and milk, skins, hair and wool. Its domesticity originated in Asia Minor and has spread both East and West.

There are many references to the goat in the earliest literature and it has a very considerable place in mythology. Pan, the Greek god, was half-goat, and the word 'capricious', meaning whimsical or irrational, is derived from *caper*, the Latin word for goat.

Sometimes regarded as evil, and maligned in various ways, the goat is an intelligent, friendly and productive animal when cared for properly.

Found in most temperate and tropical countries of the world, the goat is by nature an animal of hot and arid or mountainous areas, where it will thrive under conditions which the larger domestic animals cannot tolerate. Its propensity for eating anything and everything, and its active and agile search for food, so valuable under those circumstances, are less appropriate and when not curbed, are detrimental in areas where agriculture or afforestation is practised.

Statistics compiled by the Food and Agricultural Organization of the United Nations, show the following world goat population (1966):

Africa	108,100,000
America (North and South) . . .	44,600,000
Asia (excludes U.S.S.R. in Asia) . .	180,930,000
Australia (Oceania)	200,000
Europe (includes U.S.S.R. in Asia) .	19,851,000
Total	353,681,000

The greatest concentrations are in the Mediterranean area, parts of India, Indo-China, the West Indies and West Africa.

The number of goats in Britain is unknown as the agricultural census does not cover holdings of less than one acre on which many goats are kept. The United Nations latest estimate for the United Kingdom is 23,000.

In some countries the goat plays an important part in agriculture, whilst in others it is barely on the fringe of commercial activities. Taking the world as a whole, there is justification for stating that more than a third of its population relies on the goat rather than on cattle for milk and meat. Flesh and milk are both major products under tropical and semi-tropical conditions but milk is the more important product in temperate zones. The sale of skins for conversion into leather is an important by-product where the goat population is large. Appropriate climatic conditions are required for the production of mohair and cashmere. Mohair is a silky type of goat hair produced mainly in Turkey, South Africa, southern U.S.A. and Mexico while the more valuable cashmere is a woolly undercoat found on another breed at a height of 15,000 ft. and over in the Himalayas.

Amongst many lesser uses, the goat serves as a pack and draught animal and has even been taught to race.

In Northern Europe, it has traditionally been the poor man's cow, kept in twos and threes to produce household dairy products at a low cost where the appropriate conditions exist. This is often where the need is greatest as alternative supplies are not always available in scattered or hilly rural areas.

In Britain, more recently, the goat has become popular both as a pet and for the production of milk. Many people also enjoy breeding, improving and exhibiting goats as a hobby. Goat-keeping is undertaken in the knowledge that the dairy products will contribute to the well-being of the household and can sometimes offset the total cost of the enterprise.

An increasing number of schools own small herds which provide a centre of interest for various studies in zoology, biology, and natural history. Their care calls for close observation and the keeping of records of production, food consumption, production costs and so on; all this instils a sense of responsibility which will prove valuable later in life.

An Anglo-Nubian goatling, aged nineteen months, showing good length and topline and the very upright stance so frequently seen in this breed. Breeder: the late J. R. Egerton.

CHAPTER 2
Conformation and Structure

Ignoring breed variations which are referred to in chapter 3, the conformation sought in a female goat is shown on p.6 and in many of the illustrations. The points looked for are:

General Outline. Broadly wedge-shaped from the neck to the hips when viewed from the side or from above.

Head. Slender, long and of moderate width with a well developed muzzle. Free from horns or horny growths. Eyes large and bright. The facial line varies with the breed.

Neck and Shoulders. Long, slim neck joining tightly-knit and narrow shoulders.

Chest. Deep and wide to provide heart room.

Topline. Long and straight from the shoulders to the hips, with only a gradual fall from the hips to the tail.

Ribs and Body. Well rounded or 'sprung' with the body increasing in depth from behind the forelegs. Wide between the hips.

Legs and Feet. Body supported well by strong stout legs with good bone. Hocks carried well apart and pasterns nearly vertical. Feet sound and well-shaped.

Udder, Teats and Milk Veins. Udder spherical in shape, large, supple, and attached to the body over a large area. The teats of convenient size and shape, set well apart, pointing downwards and slightly forwards. A mature, heavy milker will possess milk veins, prominent to the touch, under the stomach.

Skin and Coat. Skin supple and coat short and glossy.

Overall Conformation and Appearance. The parts in correct proportion and a general appearance of quality.

The major faults are:

Head. Heaviness and width of skull that suggest masculinity.

Neck and shoulders. Short neck and heavy, wide shoulders.

Points of a female goat:

1. Neck
2. Shoulder
3. Ribs
4. Topline
5. Body
6. Hip
7. Rump
8. Anus
9. Vulva
10. Escutcheon
11. Stomach
12. Udder
13. Hock
14. Teat
15. Milk Veins
16. Hoof
17. Pastern
18. Knee
19. Chest
20. Muzzle
21. Facial line

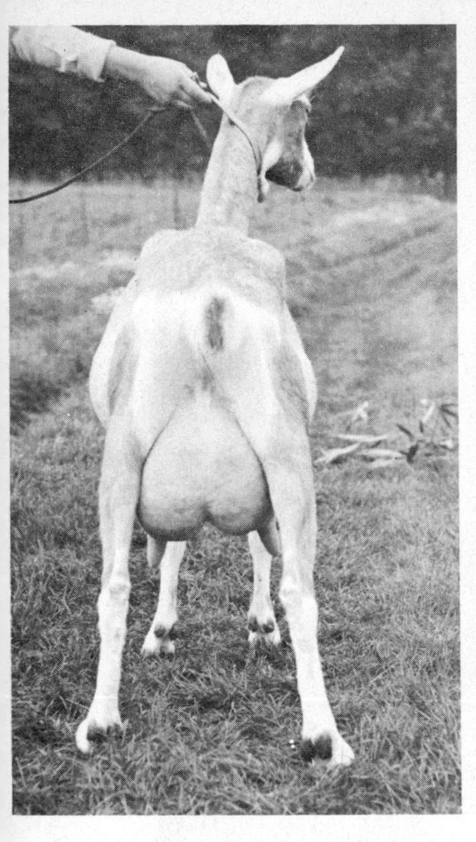

Left: prize-winning British Toggenburg female goat, showing good width across the hips, well sprung ribs, correctly shaped udder and teats, and hocks set well apart. Owner and breeder: Mrs. E. D. Clarkson
Right: Breed Champion British Saanen female goat viewed from above and from the rear, showing the desired wedge-shaped formation between the neck and the hips. Owner and breeder: Miss J. Mostyn Owen.

Topline. Drop behind the shoulders; steep fall to tail; roach or raised back.

Ribs and Body. Lack of width and depth. Narrowness between the hips.

Legs and Feet. Forelegs over at the knees, hind legs cow-hocked or sickle-shaped. Weak pasterns. Feet or hooves misshapen.

Udder. Ill-shaped and out of proportion. Prominent division between the two halves, the teats forming an elongation of the udder. Poor 'necky' attachment to or with a cavity between frontal attachment and the body. Excessive flesh tissue when milked out and lumps indicative of past or present diseased tissue. Small, over-large or bulbous teats. Extra teats, or double teats comprising two teats joined together with two orifices.

Skin and Coat. Skin tight and scurfy. Coat staring.

Overall Appearance. Coarseness and irregularity. Lack of size and bone.

The conformation sought in the male is similar, subject to the following variations:

General Outline. More size and bone, but less depth.

Head. Masculine, but some degree of femininity is preferable to coarseness. A male normally carries a beard.

Fore-quarters. Stronger than in the female.

Genital Organs. Well developed, evenly hung testicles, and rudimentary teats free from blemish.

Coat. Longer hair is frequently present, especially along the ridge of the back and on the quarters.

Weaknesses in the male are:

General Appearance. Lack of size and substance, weakness in legs and insufficient strength in hind quarters.

Coat. An older male may lose his coat and his skin may become hard.

Horns. In the wild, goats carried horns, varying greatly in size and shape, and designed primarily as a defensive weapon. In domestication horns are a nuisance, and when a polled or naturally hornless condition has arisen, endeavours have been made over the centuries to perpetuate it. Considerable success has been achieved but where efforts have been made in several countries in the last fifty years to establish homozygous or pure-polled breeds it has been found that the

An Anglo-Nubian male goat. A rear view displaying strong hind-quarters, well sprung ribs and the scrotum hung high. **Formerly owned by the** late J. R. Egerton. Breeder: Mrs. K. Carswell.

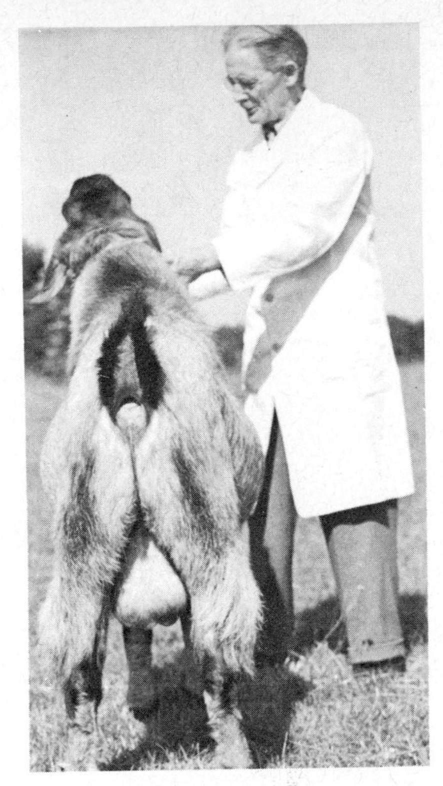

inheritance of the hornless factor is linked in this animal with the inheritance of hermaphroditism. The danger of inheriting sterility on a large scale was so great that a decision in Britain to register and breed only from hornless males was abandoned. It is found that if one parent is horned, or would have developed horns if permitted to do so, this danger is almost non-existent. In the pedigree herds and at shows, horns are very seldom seen but this result is achieved, where necessary, by the removal of the horn buds shortly after birth, by the operation known as disbudding (see page 29).

A naturally hornless adult goat has two large knob-like protuberances on the top of its head. The head of a goat that has been disbudded is almost flat.

Tassels. Some goats, more particularly those of Swiss breeds, have two appendages of gristle, covered with skin and hair and about three inches long, hanging from the neck. These are commonly known as tassels, or, in America, wattles. They serve no useful purpose and their presence or absence is ignored with the exception that they should not be seen on the Anglo-Nubian breed. Their origin is obscure but it has been suggested that they are rudimentary gills.

The goat is a ruminant and possesses four intercommunicating stomachs. When food is eaten it receives a preliminary mastication and an admixture of saliva before being passed down the gullet to the first or second stomach according to its condition. After mixing with previously ingested food and water and undergoing bacterial ferment it is regurgitated into the mouth at a convenient time for the process known as chewing the cud, before it is again swallowed and passes through the whole digestive system.

In milk-fed kids the milk passes directly into the fourth stomach. In an adult, food is likely to reach the third and fourth stomachs between two and five hours from when it is eaten, and to have left the stomachs within twenty-four hours. The excretion will commence after twelve hours, be at a maximum after forty-eight hours, but may not be complete in less than fifteen to twenty days. Greenfood speeds up the digestive process, whereas a withdrawal of roughage will impede its progress.

The teeth are a means of ascertaining the approximate age of a young goat. A 'full mouth' consists of thirty-two teeth, eight incisors or front teeth in the lower jaw and six molars or back teeth in each side of the upper and lower jaws. The incisors meet a hard pad, possessing no teeth, in the upper jaw. At birth the incisors are baby teeth which are gradually replaced by permanent incisors: the first two permanent incisors appear centrally between the age of twelve and fifteen months, the next two, on either side of the central pair, at around two years, and so on annually until the full mouth is achieved at about the age of four years.

Size is variable, dependent upon parental, environmental and nutritional factors. A combination of weight, and height at shoulder is an imperfect yardstick but can be used for comparative purposes.

Because of intensive feeding and management, the goats seen at shows in Britain are probably the largest in the world. The average weight of all adult females exhibited at one leading show over a period of eight years was 174 lb., the maximum recorded being 250 lb. and the minimum 133 lb. These figures, however, are not representative; the average for pedigree and hand-reared females may be around 140 lb. and for those with less favourable rearing, not more than 100 lb.

Subject to breed variation, prize-winning females stand at shoulder heights varying from 25 in. to 35 in.

Up to the age of one year the young of both sexes are defined as kids. A male over one year but not exceeding two years is known as a buckling and a female of the same age is known as a goatling. When they reach the age of two years goats are recognized as adults and known as male and female goats in the pedigree world – elsewhere the terms 'billy' and 'nanny' are still in common usage, while in America and in some other countries adults are known as bucks and does.

Female goats will often live ten to fourteen years and males eight to ten years, but both sexes, and particularly males, may be humanely destroyed when their effective breeding life has terminated at around eight and six years respectively.

CHAPTER 3
The Breeds

The formation of a breed may be brought about by selection or by geographical circumstances which inhibit the introduction of differing types, necessitate line-breeding – the mating of distantly related stock – and result in the fixing of type. The several quite distinct breeds found in different mountain valleys of Switzerland and the breed established on the island of Malta are examples of the latter.

Many breeds and types exist throughout the world, but are often only of local interest. The following breeds, however, have achieved international recognition and have spread beyond the named countries of origin:

Saanen (Switzerland)
Toggenburg (Switzerland)
Chamoisée or Oberhasli-Brienz (Switzerland)
Angora (Turkey)
Mamber (Syria)
Anglo-Nubian (Britain)
Britsh Alpine (Britain)
Granada (Spain)
Murcian (Spain)
Maltese (Malta)
Jumna Pari (India)
Zariby (Ethiopia)

For milk production, the Saanen has made the greatest impact, many countries having established national breeds of their own upon this blood, although not always retaining the original name. In Switzerland, improvement in productivity by selection took place simultaneously with the fixing of type, and started earlier than elsewhere. By using Swiss goats for foundation stock other countries have been able to catch up and, as in Britain, improve upon the imported stock. The Angora, bred for mohair, is the other breed of world-wide repute.

A hundred years ago, the goats in Britain were of no clearly defined type. The majority were small, with short legs, beards, 'dished' faces and horns which grew backwards then outwards. They were a mixture of grey, brown and white with no definite markings. These goats had a considerable amount of long hair on the back and quarters and often grew a woolly undercoat in the winter months.

Ireland and Wales possessed greater goat populations than England and Scotland and large herds were sent frequently from Ireland and driven across Wales and England until they found homes. The Irish and Welsh goats were often a rusty black or alternatively white, with longer legs, and horns that were less inclined to turn outwards.

With no restrictions on importation, a trickle of foreign goats of various types was then arriving – brought on ships from the East to provide milk on the journey – some were from India and others were picked up *en route*. The first Toggenburgs were imported in 1884 and the first Saanens in 1903.

The first goat show in Britain was held at the Crystal Palace in London in 1874, and this was followed by the formation of the British Goat Society in 1879. These events, combined with the fact that several titled patrons became interested and exhibited at shows, gave a considerable impetus to goat-keeping and selective breeding.

There were insufficient goats of specific types to adhere to purity of breed when the Herd Book (see p.14) was opened in 1886 by the British Goat Society and most breeders crossed the types, aiming only at good conformation and milk production. The division of classes at the earliest shows was, apart from age and sex, on a basis of horned or hornless, and entry to the Herd Book was determined in part on prizes won. Some breeders still use cross-breeding to produce the type of goat they require – for showing, or for milk production, for example. The resulting progeny were known originally as Anglo-Nubian-Swiss, but for brevity and convenience are now registered as British although the former name was more appropriate and descriptive. Goats can be graded up into this section of the Herd Book. If a female ineligible for registration is mated to a Herd Book male, the resulting female progeny are eligible for registration in the Supplementary Register. If a goat entered in the Supplementary Register is in

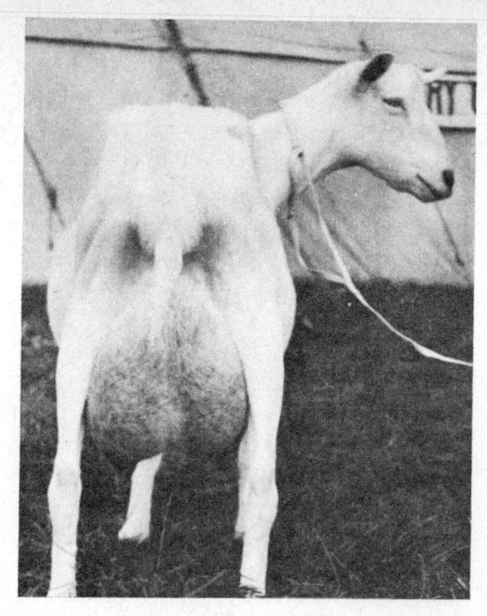

A prize-winning British female goat, possessing 2 Saanen, 3 British Saanen, 1 Toggenburg, and 2 British Toggenburg great-grandparents. Kept under backyard conditions, this goat yielded 16.8 lb. in a 24-hour recognized milking competition. Owner and breeder: Mrs. W. Cotton.

turn mated to a Herd Book male, the female progeny are eligible for the Foundation Book and the female progeny of goats entered in that Book, sired by a Herd Book male, are eligible for the Herd Book. In other words, a female must have at least six of her eight great-grandparents entered in any section of the Herd Book and a seventh in the Herd Book or Foundation Book to be eligible for the British Section. Males are ineligible for the Supplementary Register or Foundation Book and must have both parents in the Herd Book to be eligible for registration therein. Other conditions have to be met and full particulars of registration can be obtained from the British Goat Society (see p.103). Many goats entered in this British section are of similar type and possess equal milking qualities to those entered in the breed sections but it must be understood that while a goat registered as British has a pedigree of registered ancestors it is not a pedigree representing purity of breed or type and the goat may be of any type (and is likely to produce similar progeny) dependent upon percentage of breed blood.

In addition to the cross-breeds, there has been a steadily increasing interest in the pure breeds which are either directly descended or have been developed from imported stock.

Between the two World Wars efforts were made to establish by selection and to maintain the English goat as a pure breed. A separate society was formed, a Herd Book opened, and shows for this breed were held. Milk yields and lactations, however, were poor, and the breed had disappeared by 1939.

There are still a few wild goats in the mountains of Scotland and Wales and these, and a native goat still found in Norway, are of a similar type to that recognized as the English goat.

The prohibition on importation, except under special circumstances, which came into effect in 1906, has only been lifted twice since – in 1922 when 17 Toggenburgs and 29 Saanens were imported, and in 1965 when the numbers were 6 Toggenburgs and 8 Saanens. The numbers of imported animals, upon which all our pure breeds are founded, have therefore been small.

In all classes of stock it is customary to stabilize a breed by registration, only animals that comply with the conditions laid down and that are so registered being recognized as pure-bred. If all the conditions are not complied with the animal can only be described, where appropriate, as of the specified 'breed type'.

Pure breed is a relative term interpreted in different ways. In Britain what is known as a 'closed book' is applied in respect of the Toggenburg and Saanen breeds and for those sections approved imported stock and descendants containing only their blood are recognized as pure bred.

With the Anglo-Nubian, British Alpine, British Toggenburg and British Saanen, all 'made' in Britain, a minimum of seven of the eight great-grandparents must be entered in the appropriate section or sections to gain entry.

The breed sections of the Herd Book were opened as and

when sufficient stock of each type and breeding became available – Toggenburg in 1905, Anglo-Nubian in 1910, Saanen in 1922, and British Alpine, British Toggenburg and British Saanen in 1925. The more detailed conditions of entry will be found in the British Goat Society's regulations.

The breeds can be described as follows:

(a) *Toggenburg.* The well-known Swiss breed. A small light-boned goat of good conformation. The head is neat, with small, prick ears and a concave facial line. Tassels on the neck are typical. The distinctive colour can be variously described as fawn, camel, drab or mouse, with white facial stripes from above the eyes to the muzzle, around the edges of the ears, on the legs from the knees and hocks downwards, on the rump and on or about the tail (these

A Toggenburg female goat, winner of many Breed Challenge Certificates. The photograph shows the longer hair that is often carried on the flanks in this breed. Owner and breeder: Mrs. R. M. Ragg.

being known as white Swiss markings). Long hair fading to the colour of sand is often found along the back and on the flanks but less frequently than in Switzerland. This breed is larger in Britain than in its native country; breed weights for adults may average 115 lb. for females and 150 lb. for males.

The milk yield and butter-fat percentage are below the average for all breeds.

(b) *Anglo-Nubian.* Based on goats imported from the East, crossed with our mixed stock. The 459 goats registered in this section of the Herd Book when it first opened were born in the previous thirteen years and all were descended from three imported males. A large, tall goat which often has an upright stance which accentuates a tendency for the topline to drop behind the shoulder and fall steeply from the hips to the tail. The hind legs are very straight when

Head of Anglo-Nubian female goat. The roman nose and the wide ears hanging almost vertically, which are typical of the breed, are well illustrated here.

viewed from the side and are rarely cow-hocked. Depth of body is sometimes lacking. The typical features of the breed are a Roman or convex nose and pendulous ears: ideally the latter should be large, free from fold, and should fall almost perpendicularly. Colour is not fixed and can range from black to white: red and lighter tans with black markings, and mottled piebalds are quite common. Minor abnormalities occasionally seen are a wry nose, an upper jaw that is shorter than the lower jaw and a wry tail. The first is not tolerated, but the last two are usually accepted. The coat is short and glossy.

Breed average weights are females 160 lb. and males 210 lb.

The Anglo-Nubian is sometimes more noisy than other breeds, but it has a reputation for putting on flesh readily. The milk yield is below the average for all breeds but the butter-fat content is almost invariably higher, usually by at least 1 per cent. Length of lactation tends to be shorter than in other breeds.

(c) *Saanen.* This most famous of Swiss breeds only reached

A well-grown Saanen female kid, aged five months, showing excellent growth, conformation and quality. Owner and breeder: Miss J. Mostyn Owen.

Britain in sufficient numbers to maintain it as a pure breed in 1922. The specimens then imported came from Holland, which may be the reason they were bigger boned, shorter legged and heavier than the typical Swiss Saanen. They are still mostly big bodied goats, the length of leg has increased and the tendency to weakness in the hocks and pasterns is less prevalent. The head is thicker than in the Toggenburg and the facial line is usually concave or dished. Ears of medium size are carried well above the horizontal. The colour is pure white although black skin spots on the nose, eyelids, ears and udders are not objected to. The coat is normally short but a longer fringe along the back and on the flanks is occasionally seen.

Breed average weights are females 150 lb. and males 200 lb.

The breed is quiet and placid and has a high reputation for milk production and long lactation.

(d) *British Alpine.* A breed developed in Britain mainly from Toggenburg and Saanen blood: black with the usual white

A British Alpine buckling, aged eighteen months, well grown and possessing good body development. Former owner and breeder: the late J. R. Egerton.

Head study of a British Alpine female goat with the white markings which should be clearly defined on all British Alpine, Toggenburg and British Toggenburg goats.

Swiss markings. A large goat, the colouring of which catches the eye, but conformation and udder shape tend to vary widely. A short woolly undercoat often develops in winter.

(e) *British Toggenburg.* Based on the Toggenburg but with some other blood. A larger, improved version of the parent breed. The coat is short and the body colour more variable, approximating 'mil' chocolate' in some cases.

A British Toggenburg Inter-breed Champion and Breed Champion male goat which displays the size, length, level topline and bone formation sought, and the longer hair often carried by Toggenburg and British Toggenburg males. Owner and breeder: Mrs. A. Diment.

(f) *British Saanen.* Again an improved version of the parent breed, with some of the defects bred out by the introduction of other blood.

British Alpine, British Saanen and British Toggenburg goats have much in common and except for colour are very similar in appearance, closer in fact to one another than to their parent breeds. All three have ears a little larger than those of the Toggenburg and Saanen, but carried well above the horizontal. The British Toggenburg may be a little lighter than the other two breeds, but average weights for all three may be said to be 160 lb. for females and 210 lb. for males.

For milk production there is little between them – some of the heaviest milkers are found in each of these breeds.

A British Saanen Breed Champion female goat, that after first kidding yielded, officially recorded, 4840 lb. in 365 days and in a 24-hour recognized milking competition 15.2 lb. and 12.5 lb fourteen and nineteen months later respectively, without further breeding. Owner and breeder: Miss J. Gordon McLeod.

In recent years approximately 2,500 goats have been registered annually in the British Goat Society's Herd Book, the average percentage of this total entered in each Section being Toggenburg 2 per cent, Anglo-Nubian 12 per cent, Saanen 4 per cent, British Alpine 6 per cent, British Toggenburg 12 per cent, British Saanen 16 per cent and British 48 per cent.

Partial recognition has recently been given by the British Goat Society to goats known as Golden Guernseys, for which a Register has been opened. Originating on the island, partly from Anglo-Nubian stock, its main feature is its colour — a somewhat variable gold. Specimens are small and a type has not yet been clearly established.

CHAPTER 4
Goat-keeping Methods and Management

The manner in which goats are kept varies widely. Factors which influence the method used are: the nature and area of the land, the number of goats to be kept, the means of containing them within an area, and the purpose or purposes for which the goats are kept.

Housing is a necessity in Britain and is described in chapter 5.

If circumstances permitted, most goat owners would select the free range system. This requires a large area of rough, uncultivated land, such as moorland or hillside, upon which the goats can roam at will. The soil would be light and the land partially covered by scrub growth, for goats prefer feeding upon a large variety of leaves, brambles, small shrubs, weeds and short grass rather than on lush, coarse, or long grass. However, such conditions are seldom available.

Stall feeding is the name given to the system which involves permanent housing with a small, concreted yard for daily exercise. In this way goats can be kept quite successfully in a back yard provided there are no bye-laws which prohibit it and provided that the animals are not allowed to become a nuisance to neighbours. The disadvantage is that all the food the goat would find for itself on free range has to be found and carried to it, or substitutes employed.

For much of the year, woodlands, lanes and hedgerows provide a mass of food, and numerous sacks, a pair of secateurs and some means of transportation are all that is required.

Some form of compromise between these methods is generally adopted, with a grazing area of between half an acre and several acres. The warning must be given that constant use of a very small area of grass is highly unsatisfactory, particularly if the land tends to be wet; it becomes a breeding ground for intestinal parasites to which goats are subject and which can quickly undermine their health (see chapter 10).

The objective should be not less than a quarter of an acre per goat and the area available should be divided into several small paddocks which can be grazed and then rested, on a rotation system, but never permitting the grass to become rank or be fouled heavily by poultry or other stock. The goat is not an instrument for removing long and unwanted grass, and will not serve that purpose.

In country districts it is often possible to supplement controlled grazing by taking goats for walks along little-used lanes, particularly where there are wide grass verges, on commons, in woodlands, on the embankments of disused railway lines and over agricultural land where no harm can be done to growing crops, but permission should be obtained where necessary. Goats soon learn to follow, feeding as they go, and can be taught to respond to the call of an attendant. Thus the owner does not have to collect the food.

A satisfactory means of containing goats when they are unattended is essential, for they are very apt to stray, will find a way through most live hedges and often destroy these within a few years by eating the bark. Young trees may suffer the same fate.

A permanent chain-link fence, with a minimum height of 3 ft. 6 in. is strongly recommended. A multi-strand wire fence or woven wire sheep fence is cheaper and may serve the purpose if strained taut and well supported by frequent posts.

Chestnut pale fencing, unless very tall, can be dangerous should a goat attempt to jump it and get its head caught between two pales, above the top wire.

Electric fencing can be used as a temporary measure or to divide grazing paddocks but is less reliable on the perimeter. Goats will go over or under a single, electrified wire and where this method is employed three wires should be used, at some 3 in. above shoulder, chest and knee height respectively, although the lowest one may not need to be alive. The goats should be encouraged to come into contact with the electrified wires when they are first introduced, as when they do so gently, they realize the source of the mild shock and tend to avoid it in future. A necessary precaution is to ensure that grass and other natural growth does not come in contact with the wires and short the circuit.

The traditional method of preventing goats from straying is tethering and this enables some use to be made of unfenced waste lands, such as roadside verges, without an attendant, but the practice is unsatisfactory for several reasons.

Even when precautions are taken, there is always a danger of the tethering chain becoming wound up or entangled and of the goat's movements being severely restricted. It also gives the animal no opportunity to seek shelter from rain or excessive sun and is apt to result in more grass being soiled than is consumed.

Where a tether must be used it should comprise a strong but light chain, 10-12 ft. long, with a 3 in. spring hook and a 3 in. swivel at each end, to fasten to the collar and pin respectively. The pin should be a steel rod not less than 18 in. long, pointed at one end and with the head at the other end shaped in a way suitable for hammering it into the ground and designed with a loop to turn as the goat moves around the perimeter of the area to which it is confined. Any pails or other possible obstacles should be placed on the perimeter and the position of the tether should be moved two or three times each day.

Whatever method of goat-keeping is adopted it reduces costs considerably if some of the food required can be grown on the holding, either in the garden or on a small area developed as arable land. Few will contemplate growing cereals or make any quantity of hay and usually it is the following succulent green crops and roots that are home produced:

CROP	REMARKS
Carrots	Best on light soil.
Clover, Red	For feeding green or as hay.
Comfrey, Giant Russian	Will grow anywhere and stand for ten years. Takes two years to establish, then five cuts per annum.

Kale, Marrow stem	Susceptible to 'fly' in seedling stage and to damage by snow. Limit thinning to reduce thickness of stems.
Kale, Thousand head	Susceptible to 'fly' but less damaged by snow and frost.
Kale, Perpetual	Suitable for very small plots.
Lucerne	Needs clean land. Stands five years and withstands drought. One late cut first year, three cuts per annum subsequently.
Maize, Green	Very susceptible to frost.
Mangolds	Feed after Christmas.
Sugar Beet and Fodder Beet	Grown basically for the roots. If tops are fed, wash and allow to wilt before feeding.
Swedes	Feed from late autumn.

While kids that are reared on their dams should be handled frequently and from an early age to ensure their docility, those that are hand-reared are always exceedingly tame and easy to manage. When lifting a kid, one arm should be placed behind its hind legs and then be brought under the body to take the weight, with the legs parallel with the underside of the body, and the forequarters lifted in the same way with the other arm. All goats should be accustomed to wearing a collar and it is usual for adult goats to wear one continuously. The collar, ideally of leather, and approximately ¾ in. wide for an adult, should have a half ring to which a leather lead or light chain can be attached. As there is a slight risk that an animal can be caught up in a fence or elsewhere by its collar some breeders prefer not to use them regularly with the more active young stock.

A prospective goat-keeper, or schools contemplating goat-keeping should realize that the keeping of any animal, and particularly one that produces milk, makes a considerable call, at regular hours, on the time of the person or persons responsible for its welfare. It cannot be a five-day week job or a term-time project only, and for those not interested in livestock it can become very irksome. On the other hand the burden will rest lightly on the shoulders of animal lovers who will find that the understanding which develops between goats and their owners and the pleasures to be found in goat-keeping will more than compensate for the hard work and the disappointments that every stock-keeper has to face.

The first daily task is that of feeding. The routine will depend on whether the goats are picking up their food out-of-doors or whether everything is carried to them. In summer, with free range and open-fronted shelters available, it may be necessary to bring the goats in twice a day only, to feed some concentrates and hay, and it is common practice to let this coincide with milking. Bottle-fed kids will require their feeds four or three times a day, according to age (see page 65). In winter the weather may prevent the goats going out for more than an hour or two, and their food should then be given to them at least three times a day – preferably four. While it is desirable to keep regular hours the precise time-table can be prepared to suit the goat-keeper, bearing in mind that the length of time between milkings should not be more than fourteen hours and that the evening and first morning kid feeds should not be more than twelve hours apart.

Regularity in milking times is also most desirable. Milking is a simple operation which can be learned easily. Bring the thumb and first finger together at the neck of the teat and then progressively bring the remaining fingers close to the hand, thereby squeezing the milk out of the orifice at the end of the teat, without any pulling motion. Milking should be carried out speedily with both hands. The use of the thumb and forefinger alone should be seen only in 'stripping' – the drawing off of the last drops of milk. First kidders, whose teats may be small and difficult to grasp, may present a little more difficulty, especially as they may be unaccustomed to having their udders and teats handled. Gentle perseverance is necessary and, as with all milking, treat the udder as the tender vessel it is, massaging it for a moment or two as a

The process of milking. With the teat held between the thumb and first finger, the remaining fingers are closed progressively to squeeze the milk from the orifice at the end of each teat. The grip is then relaxed and the process repeated, squeezing each teat alternatively.

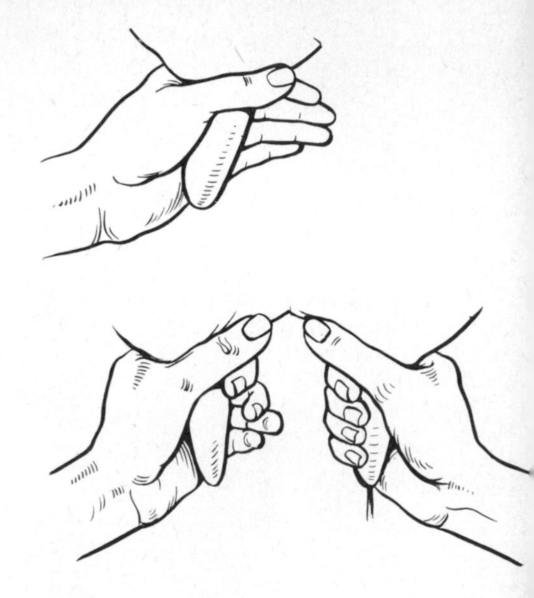

warning that the process of milking is about to commence.

Goats can be milked by machine but the numbers involved seldom justify the rather expensive equipment and the time taken to clean it after milking.

Absolute cleanliness must be maintained. Washing the udder is seldom necessary: when it is desirable to wipe it down, use a damp disposable paper towel. The first squirts of milk from each teat should be directed into a strip cup and discarded, and all milking utensils should be sterilized and kept free from dust between milkings.

Milking pails, preferably stainless steel or enamelled, should be of about one gallon capacity and with a base as wide as the open top to prevent it falling over.

Hoof trimming must be done not less than once a month. The goat seldom has sufficient exercise on hard surfaces to keep down the horny growth which covers the sides of the hooves. As a result this grows inwards under the sole and if not cut regularly tends to deform the foot. A sharp knife is

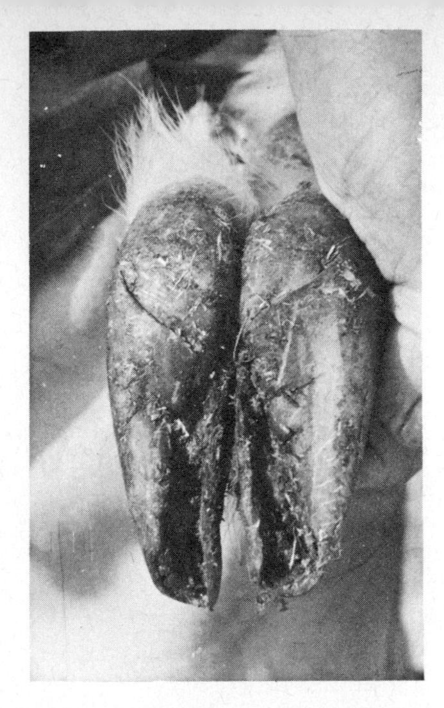

An overgrown hoof which is hiding the sole and requires trimming.

the best tool for the task, but the inexperienced sometimes prefer to use secateurs. The goat should be tied by the neck alongside a wall. The operator, facing the opposite direction, then lifts each foot backwards and upwards in turn, and with the foot held between the knees, cuts away towards the point of the foot until the horny growth is flush with the bottom of the sole. The heel may also need trimming and this must be pared very carefully and gradually so as to improve its shape but at the same time avoid drawing blood. Novices can watch demonstrations of hoof trimming at goat club meetings.

Grooming with a stiff dandy brush and a fine-toothed steel comb will help to eliminate the scurf which is often prevalent when the old coat is being shed in the spring. Extensive grooming in the winter tends to brush out any warm, woolly undercoat which some goats develop in the autumn, and consequently should be avoided. There is nothing better than a wash-leather for rubbing down and for obtaining a good gloss on the coat.

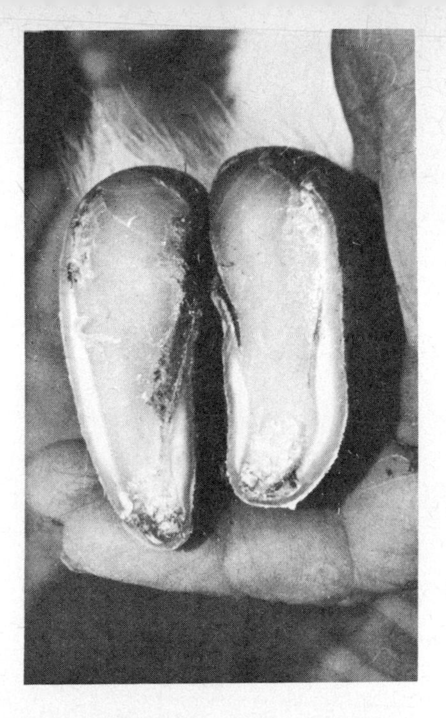

The hoof and sole as they should appear after trimming.

The keen breeder will regard the disbudding of any naturally horned kids that are to be reared as an essential feature of good management. It involves the removal of the horn buds by burning them off with a hot iron or a caustic material.

The hot iron method is generally preferred and is carried out with a goat disbudding iron. Having ascertained, without doubt, that the kid will develop horns if the buds are not removed (see page 62) the procedure is to clip the hair away entirely from an area about 1 in. in diameter around each bud. The kid must be firmly held by an assistant in such a way that the head will be motionless while the operator applies the disbudding iron. It is essential that the iron is red hot when it is applied, with the depression in the head of the iron exactly central over the horn bud, and it must be held there, in full contact, but without pressure, for precisely six seconds. The iron must then be re-heated and applied to the second horn bud. When this has been done, it will be found that a ring has been burned round each horn bud which remains as a small core which has in turn to be gently burned off with the edge of the iron after it has again been re-heated. The secret of success is a really red-hot iron at all times, the head held absolutely firm, and cool precision by the operator. The operation should take place between four and seven days after birth.

The alternative to the hot iron method is the application of a caustic material after the buds have received the same preliminary preparation. It can be a proprietary caustic disbudding stick or a dehorning collodion, both available from agricultural chemists. With a slightly moistened disbudding

Disbudding with a caustic stick, which should be wrapped in foil, to avoid damaging the hand, and moistened on the damp cotton wool. The hair has been clipped away from the horn buds to which the caustic is then applied.

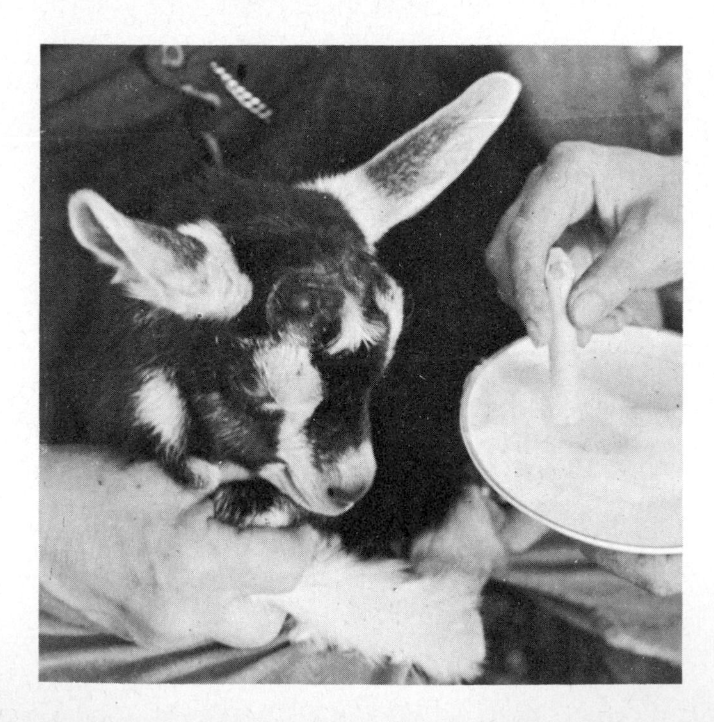

stick, the horn buds are dabbed lightly until dampness and a blistered effect is achieved over an area about ¾ in. in diameter on and around each bud, without breaking the skin. With a collodion it is painted over the same area and allowed to dry. Both materials should be fresh each year. Detailed instructions are issued with the materials, which should be applied on the third or fourth day and may not be effective if applied later, particularly in the case of male kids.

A short period of pain is inevitable, but with the hot iron method this appears to be only during the seconds of the initial applications of the iron, while the effect of the caustic materials is felt over a longer period.

While disbudding is a simple operation it is an unpleasant task and if not carried out properly can disfigure the animal for life. An experienced operator should be watched before carrying out the operation. The law provides that the hot iron method must be carried out under local anaesthetic when applied to calves but this does not apply to kids. Dehorning by the sawing off of horns under an anaesthetic can be carried out by a vet later in life but it is not recommended.

Goats in Britain which are officially milk recorded are tattooed in the left ear by the British Milk Marketing Board, and while it is not compulsory for registered goats to be so marked there is a growing tendency for this to be done on a voluntary basis. The British Goat Society is prepared to allot identification letters to a breeder or a club, to which are added numerals to identify the animal and a final letter to indicate the year of birth – 'A' refers to 1966, 'B' to 1967 and so on. These letters and numerals are made up in metal pins which are impressed into the inside of the right ear by the use of forceps, and indelible marking paste or ink is rubbed well into the pin pricks. The setting of the letters and numerals should be tested on a piece of paper to ensure that they are set correctly. The ear should be cleaned with surgical spirit before the impress is made and care taken to avoid piercing any main veins. The forceps can sometimes be obtained on loan from a local club. Black ears present a problem, even with coloured inks, but ear tabs tend to be torn out of the ear.

If the ear-marking is done before the kid is registered, the number is recorded on the Herd Book card.

The practice of keeping records in a book similar to a desk diary will prove invaluable. In this should be recorded births, deaths, 'heat' periods, matings, kiddings, changes in feeding, marked fluctuations in milk yield, medicinal treatments, weights, disbuddings and all information of that nature. Records of the milk yield of each goat on one given day in each week should be recorded in this book if more elaborate milk recording, official or private, is not carried out.

One form of record that is compulsory by law in Britain is the keeping of a Movement of Livestock Book, in which must be recorded movements of goats, and certain other animals, on and off the holding. Full particulars may be obtained from any police station, and the book must be available for inspection by the police at any time.

CHAPTER 5
Housing

A site that receives plenty of sunlight, stands high in relationship to adjoining land, adjoins a convenient paddock and has a hard vehicular approach, is most suitable.

The nearer the house the easier it is for the owner to attend to the animals. The entrances should be firm and dry under all weather conditions, and it is convenient if one or two concreted exercising yards, with substantial permanent fencing, and gates in appropriate places, can adjoin the goat house.

Goats seek shelter from rain and cold sooner than most farm animals and although some, particularly those with long hair, may become acclimatized to wet weather, good results call for adequate shelter; it need not be elaborate.

In summer open-fronted shelters can be made from baled straw and polythene, strengthened with timber or sheep netting, and for a single goat, a garden shed, 6 ft. x 4 ft. that possesses a window can suffice.

Where several goats are to be kept, thought must be given to converting any existing accommodation, such as farm buildings, stables or poultry houses, or providing a new building, and the following suggestions should be considered.

Materials will depend upon the size of the building – wood for a small house and brick or concrete blocks for a larger one. The floor should be of an impervious material, probably concrete. If hollow breeze blocks or land drain pipes are laid in parallel lines below the concrete this will help retain even temperatures and a waterproof membrane through it will prevent any dampness rising. With goat excreta normally in pelleted form, drainage is less important than in a cow house. Provide for slight falls to a passage way which can be 2 in. lower than the adjoining loose boxes or stalls and also have a slight fall to the drain, which must be fitted with a suitable trap. By this means comparatively narrow gulleys can be avoided. Any roofing material, such as galvanized iron, that gives rise to condensation, must be avoided.

Light and air are important and can best be provided by hopper-type windows opening inwards and with cheeks to prevent down draughts. Light can always be supplemented by the introduction of transparent roofing sheets. Two or three adjustable wall gratings, for ventilation in bad weather, and outlet ventilation in the roof, should be provided; all ventilation points should be at least 4 ft. 6 in. above ground level. Stable type doors, not less than 3 ft. wide, are recommended.

Size and layout must be dependent upon the number of goats to be accommodated, but it is false economy to cut this to the barest minimum. Where adaptation must suffice it may be necessary to use three or four different buildings, but where the accommodation can be provided under one roof there will be a great saving in labour.

Most owners prefer to provide a loose box, about 5 ft. x 5 ft. for each adult, and two or three such individual boxes are in any case necessary for use at kidding time, or in the event of illness. It is customary to provide two communal loose boxes, one for goatlings and one for female kids. It is necessary to ensure that a 'bully' does not make such arrangements unsatisfactory.

In a large house a central passageway between two rows of boxes may be provided solely for feeding purposes, entry to the boxes and cleaning out being effected from a perimeter passage round the inside walls of the house. More frequently it is necessary to make one passageway, which should be between 4 ft. and 5 ft. wide, to serve both purposes, in which case it should be free of food and water receptacles.

The tying of goats in stalls is not recommended but where necessary the stalls should be 2 ft. 6 in. wide and about 3 ft. 6 in. deep.

The accommodation required by the goats must include facilities for milking and milk weighing as well as storage space for foodstuffs (including hay and other bulk foods), litter and tools. A door leading to a small section of the building, otherwise completely divided off, to serve as a simple dairy, with provision for the immediate cooling of milk, washing, sterilizing and storage of all milk utensils, and

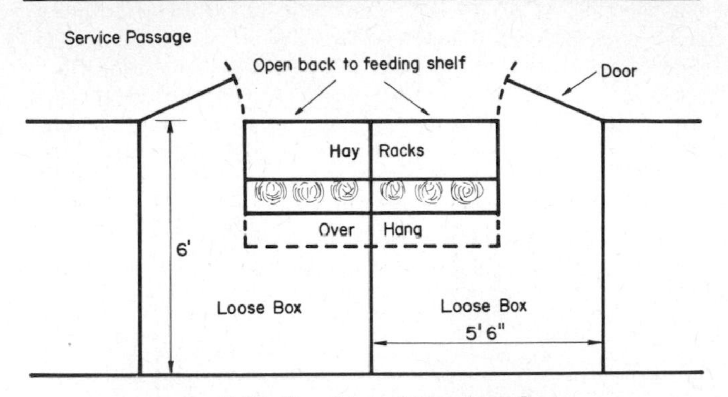

Sketch Plan of two adjoining Loose Boxes

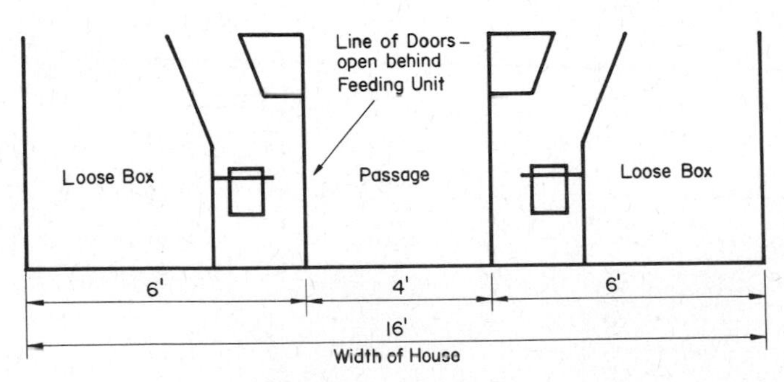

Line Sketch showing Section through Goat House

Line sketches illustrating the incorporation of the suggested feeding panel or unit in loose boxes. The plan of the two adjoining boxes shows the appropriate layout. The section through the goat house indicates the width necessary to have two rows of loose boxes facing one another, with a suitable passage between them.

the heating of milk for bottle feeding is extremely useful. Where only three or four goats are kept it is often necessary for this work to be carried out in the owner's house.

The front elevation and both ends should be faced with sheet metal or plywood, but two panels can run continuously to serve adjoining boxes. Three pails are placed behind and below the apertures and held in place by dropping them in holes, centralized behind each aperture in a shelf 22 in. above floor level. The pails are intended for concentrates, roots etc. and water respectively. The back should be left open to give access to pails. The distance between the facing panel and the rack (18 in.) is important, to permit the goat to feed freely without head or ears touching the panel. The rack, for hay or greenfood, should be faced with $\frac{3}{8}$ in. iron bars, 2½ in. apart with the back and ends again of sheet metal or plywood. With the panel face 3 ft. wide, the ends will provide necessary support for the rack and pail shelf.

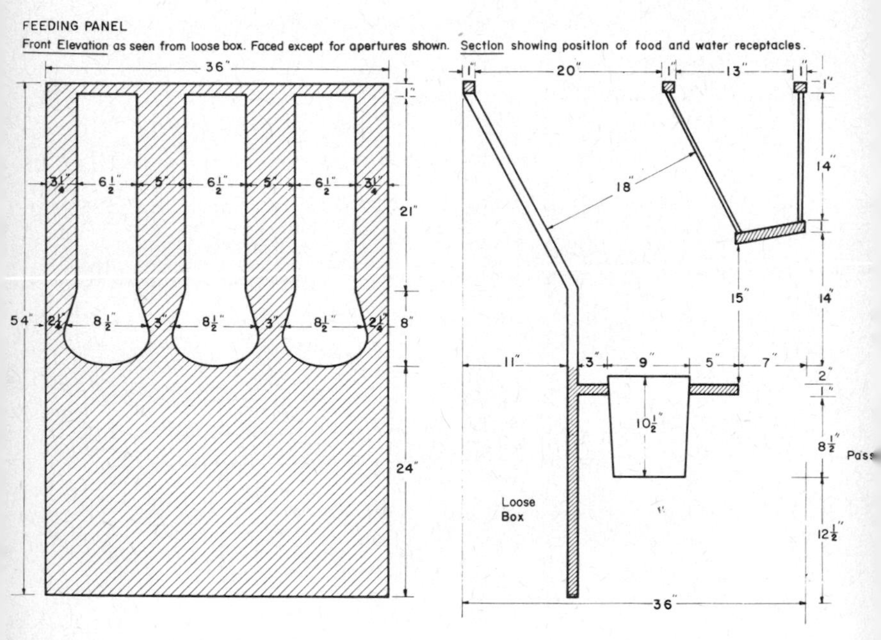

FEEDING PANEL
Front Elevation as seen from loose box. Faced except for apertures shown. Section showing position of food and water receptacles.

The provision of electric light and piped water in the goat house is well worth the investment.

Loose-box walls should be not less than 4 ft. high and as goats are curious as well as fond of company they should be enabled to see around them. If provision is not made for this they will place their forefeet on any available batten or ledge, or in any food receptacle that will enable them to see over the division. Wood is the traditional and cheapest material with $\frac{3}{8}$ in. vertical iron bars let into the wood from a height of 2 ft. or 2 ft. 6 in., not more than 3 in. apart and held in place by a wooden top rail. Light tubular steel divisons would be an improvement as goats tend to chew wood which is also difficult to keep clean. Wood, if used, should always be well planed and heavily creosoted. If the bottom of the partition is kept 6 in. off the ground this will preserve it and facilitate cleaning. Box doors, not less than 2 ft. 3 in. wide, should be on strong strap hinges and should have a self-fastening device or fasten with a bolt fitting on the outside.

Loose pails made of plastic or rubber are preferable to metal pails for food and water receptacles. They are easier to keep clean than fixed receptacles. Pails must not be stood on the floor of the box or they will be turned over or the contents fouled by droppings. These receptacles, together with a rack for feeding hay, can be placed behind a feeding panel as shown on p.36. This unit should be incorporated as a box wall adjoining the door and abutting on the passage from which it can be easily serviced without entering the box. The goat has to put its head through apertures in the front of the panel to reach either the rack or the pails. Any hay pulled from the rack will fall into the feed pail rather than on to the floor. In the simplest form of goat-house, one or two apertures are made in the loose-box door or wall adjoining the passage and the pails are hung on the passage side, again to facilitate feeding without entering the box, but this practice greatly reduces the effective width of the passage and has other disadvantages. If the portions of the panel which slope into the box are made separately, they can be removed to accommodate a horned goat. Panel, door and posts will require an

A device for holding a goat by its neck between stanchions to ensure equal feeding opportunities in a communal box. It can be adapted to hold a goat on a bench when milking is taking place.

A simple goat house in which the goats place their heads through holes in the loose-box doors to feed from pails, held in place by collapsible metal rings on the passage side of each door. On the extreme right is a milk weighing machine from which the milk bucket hangs.

overall width of 5 ft. 6 in. and doors should be hung in line with the rear of the rack to open to 180°. The only other loose box fitting required is a metal holder for the mineral lick. Hay nets are not recommended as it is too easy for the goat to get caught up in them.

In stalls a goat is best fastened by a short length of chain about 18 in. long, fitted with spring hooks and swivels, one end being fastened to the collar and the other to a vertical iron bar, 15-18 in. long, bolted to but slightly away from the stall division (if a tubular division the ring could be on one of the vertical bars). Such an arrangement enables the goat to reach up to the hay rack and to lie down comfortably without danger of it getting over the division or backing out of the stall.

In the larger boxes for goatlings or kids, wooden sleeping benches are often provided. A height of 9 in. is appropriate for goatlings, but 18 in. is preferred for kids as they often choose, when young, to lie under rather than on top of the bench. Such benches should be made in sections to facilitate removal for cleaning. Wooden structures or crates for jumping on or sheltering under should also be provided in exercising yards, where a covered feeding rack is also an asset.

For reasons stated on page 50, a male goat or goats should be housed in a separate building away from the main goat

A communal loose box for goatlings or female kids. Kids will often prefer to sleep under than on the raised sleeping bench.

house and it is particularly important that the facilities provided should make it possible to feed and water without entering the box or house.

While some owners like to sit on a low stool and milk at ground level in the individual boxes, a separate milking bench to which each goat goes in turn to be milked is often more convenient. It should be 12-15 in. off the ground, with a step at the rear end to assist the heavier goats to mount it, while at the other end a yoke-fastening arrangement (see p. 38) will enable the animal to be held firmly by the neck as may be necessary with a first kidder unaccustomed to being milked. If the bench is about 2 ft. wide the milker can sit sideways on it and get very close to the udder: the goat's left flank should be alongside the wall, the milker then reaching the far teat with the right hand, which most people find easier.

In an earlier paragraph it was suggested that the floor might be of concrete – the cheapest non-absorbent material. Concrete is cold, however, and should not be used without some further covering, particularly for an animal which prefers a hard dry bed and will scrape away a thin litter to find one. Any form of wood which covers the whole of the floor eventually becomes saturated with urine and is unhygienic. One alternative is to cover the floor with an inch or two of peat or sawdust and a good layer of straw. This should be too thick to be scraped away: the excreta, both liquid and solid, will be absorbed by the litter and if the straw is forked over daily there will be no need to replace the bedding for several weeks. Another alternative is to provide in one corner a wooden bed, approximately 3 ft. x 2 ft. covered with asphalt tiles or a thick cork or rubber mat, and raised a few inches above ground level to isolate the goat from the concrete. It will normally be used in cold weather. This method requires no litter but involves daily brushing out and it will be more difficult to keep the goat clean.

If several goats are kept, a light wheelbarrow, stiff broom, a fork and disinfectant will be needed for keeping the goat house clean. Other items of equipment that will be needed are mentioned in the appropriate chapters.

CHAPTER 6
Feeding

A goat will eat a great variety of substances (including some not recognized as food stuffs!), but at the same time be fastidious, and the food must be clean and fresh.

Research work on its nutritional needs has been very limited. As a result feeding is based largely on practical experience and close observation of appetite, condition and milk yield.

Food is necessary to maintain bodily functions and also to supply the nutrients which subsequently may be converted into milk or progeny.

Good hay should be regarded as the basic need and is essential for satisfactory results. The main supporting foods can be classified, with one or two exceptions, as bulky succulents or concentrates.

The succulents, which have a moisture content of between 75 and 90 per cent, should be considered first for, with hay, they can meet the maintenance requirements and provide the necessary vitamins or the raw materials from which these are developed. They can often be home grown or purchased comparatively cheaply, and in appropriate quantity they satisfy the appetite and the digestive system. Grass, rough grazing and browsing, are the most common succulents available. Kale, lucerne and mangolds are prominent amongst many others, most of which are valuable in season.

The snag is that large quantities of such feeds – quantities often beyond the appetite and the digestive capacity – may be required to replace the nutrients lost in milk production, and it becomes necessary to substitute concentrates for some of the succulents.

Concentrates are, in the main, processed dried grain, with a moisture content of between 10 and 15 per cent, and have a greater nutritional value in a more concentrated form. Crushed or rolled oats, flaked maize, broad bran and dairy nuts are typical examples. The first three are known as 'straight' feeds as each is the product of one type of cereal: the last named may contain a large number of ingredients compounded into cake form to a prescribed analysis. Such foods have to be purchased and are expensive, but they are convenient to handle and the quantity fed can be easily controlled.

Trace minerals must not be forgotton. These are present in most green foods and are incorporated in dairy nuts, but a mixed mineral lick should always be available and for heavy milkers a proprietory mineral powder should be added to the concentrates.

From the foregoing remarks it will be appreciated that the diet should consist of more than one type of food. A goat will not thrive on concentrates alone, roughage – in the form of hay and succulents – is essential, and a good milker needs a higher percentage of protein than is found in most roughage.

The following foods are widely used by goat-keepers in Britain. The asterisks indicate their palatability, xxx = excellent, xx = good, x = fair.

Hay. (xxx, xx or x) This can be made from various crops. The highest mark is given to that made from sanfoin, clover or a mixture of clover and Italian rye grass. That made from meadow grass follows. The quality of the hay depends largely upon a number of circumstances including cutting before flowering and getting the crop dried and quickly under cover. Much of the value is in the leaf and every effort must be made to avoid losing this at any stage. Poor musty hay, in which the nutrients are about half those in a good sample, is unpalatable and should be avoided.

SUCCULENTS

Green leaves, twigs and young bark (scrub growth or brushwood). (xxx) The goat's first choice of natural food, and in the following approximate order of preference – elm, ash, willow, hazel, oak, brambles, ivy, holly, gorse. Rhododendron and yew must be avoided (see page 73). Many weeds including docks, thistles, nettles and hogweed are eaten with relish.

Grass. (xxx or xx according to quality) Herbage leys and rye grass most suitable. Preferred short – long and coarse grass will be avoided. High feeding value in spring but this falls away subsequently.

Green leguminous plants. (xxx) Primarily the clovers, lucerne and sanfoin. Perennial crops which can be cut and fed or grazed where they stand. Will provide three or four crops.

Kale. (xxx) A main standby in autumn and early winter. Thousand head or marrow stem preferred. Leaves can be stripped off and fed without stems which are best sliced before feeding.

Other brassicas. (xx) Open-leaved cabbages, sprout tops, broccoli, leaves of cauliflowers etc. are often available throughout the year. The drumhead cabbages have lower feeding value but stand the winter with less damage. Can cause indigestion if fed in large quantities.

Roots. (xxx or xx) Those most frequently used are mangolds, sugar beet, fodder beet (a continental cross between sugar beet and mangolds), swedes and carrots. Contain a large percentage of water but available in winter when other succulents are in short supply. Most should be lifted in autumn and clamped to give protection against frost. Mangolds should be allowed a ripening period and not be used until after Christmas. Potatoes, if fed in quantity, should be steamed or boiled and dried off with bran or weatings.

Garden and Kitchen Waste. (xxx) Garden waste, including greens, pea haulm, roots, fruit-tree prunings, windfall apples, hedge trimmings etc. are enjoyed, as are potato peelings, chit potatoes, pea pods, and dry bread (preferably crisped) from the kitchen.

CONCENTRATES

Cereals. (xxx or xx according to variety) Oats, maize, beans and wheat by-products are most suitable: barley less so. If fed whole, there is a tendency for all grains to pass through the body undigested. Consequently grains should be rolled, crushed, cracked, split or treated in a similar way. Maize is best fed in the cooked, flaked form, and is then perhaps the most popular goat feed. The soya bean is fed as a coarse meal. Broad bran, the rolled skin of the grain, and weatings are wheat by-products, while dried brewers' grains and malt culms are sometimes obtainable locally. Protein content varies widely.

N.B. Cereals are seldom fed 'straight'. The practice is to feed a mixture of several cereals with or without some dairy or oil cake nuts, or dry sugar beet pulp, and to change the mixture periodically.

Three suitable mixtures are:

		Parts by weight
1.	Flaked Maize	1
	Rolled Oats	1
	Broad Bran	1
	Linseed Cake	1
2.	Rolled Oats	1
	Kibbled Beans	1
	Groundnut cake	1
	Flaked Maize	1
3.	Soya Bean Meal	1
	Flaked Maize	2
	Broad Bran	1

Dairy Nuts or Coarse Dairy Meals. (xxx or xx) These, in various proprietary makes, have the advantage that they are correctly balanced for milk production, with a guaranteed content. They may contain a mixture of ten or more ingredients and incorporate necessary minerals. Mostly palatable but a high fish meal content in some is objected to. Different types are manufactured to offset varying values in grass.

Suger Beet Pulp. (xxx) The molassed, dry type preferred. Feeding can be treated as a concentrate or be scalded or soaked and then brought to a crumbly consistency by dusting off with weatings, bran or grass meal. Available also in nut form.

Dried Grass Meal. (x) High protein content. Very powdery. Sometimes fed in the form of pony nuts or sprinkled on cut roots.

Oil Cakes. (xxx or xx according to variety) Those most used for goats are decorticated groundnut cake, linseed cake and decorticated cotton cake. Protein content varies between one cake and another. Linseed cake, with an exceptionally high oil content is helpful in obtaining bloom and condition.

When a goat is browsing, or grazing, it is not possible to weigh or even estimate the weight of succulent roughages it consumes, but provided it eats the other allowances it is likely to adjust the succulents to its need.

Subject to what has been said earlier, half the concentrates should be fed in the early morning and the other half in the late afternoon, preferably during milking as this helps to keep the goats quiet. With the heavy milkers, it may be desirable to feed some in the middle of the day. In the summer, a small feed of hay before going out on to lush, succulent food may help to prevent over-eating and also to maintain good butterfat levels in the milk. In winter, the bulk food should be fed not less than three times daily with the last feed as late as possible.

All concentrates should be fed in clean receptacles. Hay, greens and similar bulk foods are best fed from racks which will prevent the food being dropped to the ground and trampled on.

Slice roots or cut them in halves and feed in buckets with the flat cut uppermost; alternatively they can be cut in fingers. They should always be freshly cut. Oil or other cakes can be eaten more readily when they are in small nut or cube form. Meals, except for the coarsest, tend to develop into a paste in the mouth and are best fed sprinkled on moist foods such as cut roots or soaked suger beet pulp.

Quantities fed must depend upon many circumstances, for in addition to the weight of the goat and its milk yield,

Feeding chart showing approximate quantities of food required daily by goats weighing between 130 and 150 lb. that are dry or yielding one of the quantities of milk specified at the head of the columns. The figures in any one vertical column represent the quantities in lbs. of the feeding stuffs listed on the left, and the five columns under each yield are alternatives.

Description of Food	Dry*					Yield 2½ lb*					Yield 5 lb*					Yield 7½ lb					Yield 10 lb					Yield 12½ lb					Yield 15 lb				
	1	2	3	4	5	6	7	8	9	10	11	12	13	14	15	16	17	18	19	20	21	22	23	24	25	26	27	28	29	30	31	32	33	34	35
Brushwood or Scrub Growth	3				2		1			2		4	1		5			3	3		3		2		2		2			2					
Clover (Red), Lucerne or Sanfoin							5					4					4						4				6						6		
Grass, Spring or Early Summer	8	10					6			8		5		11			6	7			6						4			6		8	7	10	
Grass, other Seasons			4	2	3			5	2				3		5					5		4									5				
Maize, Green			3					3							4					5			5												
Kale			4	2		5		2	5		4		5							4			3			5			4		8				
Cabbages, and other Brassicas		3					2			4				3				3							3			2							3
Roots				5		4			5		3		5			8								6				3							
Silage					3				3						5				3																
Hay, Red Clover													2																					4	
Hay, Lucerne (very good)																3			2	2				3	2	3		4	3						2
Hay, Seeds Mixture											3							2				2	3								4				
Hay, Meadow (very good)									2			3									2						3			4		3	3		
Hay, Meadow (average)	1	1	1	1	2	2	1	2		2				2			3																		
Sugar Beet Pulp				2		2										2			1			3		1	3	2		2	4						3
Concentrate Mixture, Dairy Nuts or Dairy Meal								1			2		1	1	1	1	2	2	2	2	3	2	3	3	2	3	3	3	2	3	4	5	4	4	4

*if in kid, extra food should be given — see page 57

factors such as the system of management and the varying nutritional value of many foods have to be taken into account. As a rough indication a Feeding Chart is printed on page 46, showing five suggested alternative diets for each of six goats with differing yields. In each case the appropriate nutrients are provided for and the consumption is likely to be within the appetite and digestive powers of a goat weighing between 130 lbs. and 150 lbs. It will be seen that as the yield increases so do the concentrates and other high protein foods. Any quantities can be altered at will provided that any substitution provides the same nutrients and bulk.

Other guide lines which may be of interest:

(a) Adequate free range and hay ad lib should meet the maintenance requirements for body weight and the first 2½ lbs. of milk.
Add 6 ozs. of concentrates for each additional 1 lb. of milk.

(b) Maximum Daily Consumption
if only one type of food available:
Hay 5 lbs. or
Succulents 25 lbs. or
Concentrates 6 lbs.

(c) Daily Consumption of Dry Matter:
Between 4 lbs. and 9 lbs.

(d) Rough equivalent Feeding Values:

8 lbs.	Dairy Nuts
10 lbs.	Flaked Maize
15 lbs.	Good Hay
15 lbs.	Molassed Sugar Beet Pulp
15 lbs.	Broad Bran
25 lbs.	Poor Hay
80 lbs.	Kale
90 lbs.	Cabbages
100 lbs.	Mangolds

Clean water is important and soft water is preferable to hard. If the goats do not have water always available, it should be offered at least four times daily and the consumption by a heavy milker may be as much as five gallons daily. The addition of a little salt or a handful of oatmeal sprinkled on the water will increase consumption. In cold weather, the water should have the chill taken off it.

The special requirements of kids and goats in kid are referred to in the appropriate chapters.

Those seeking further information are referred to the Ministry of Agriculture, Fisheries and Food Bulletin No. 48, Rations for Livestock, which, while not mentioning goats, gives the analysis and other information about various foods.

CHAPTER 7
The Male Goat

The choice of a male goat is not an easy one for the serious breeder attempting to improve stock. Comparatively few owners limit their goats to one breed, and there is not the uniformity of conformation, type and production that exists in many classes of stock. Majority opinion is opposed to crossing the breeds. In most cases there is a desire to increase milk yield and butter-fat content; many will seek some improvement in shape of udder and teats and there are likely to be at least one or two points of conformation or breed characteristics that need to be improved. Ideally one might wish to select a different mate for each female according to individual defects or weaknesses but that is seldom practicable when ownership of the male is involved, and the choice of goats at stud in any one area is not often as large as might be wished.

A common procedure is to try and find what is known as a 'proven sire' of the appropriate breed. This is not the same thing as a proved stock-getter (a term used to indicate that the animal has proved his ability to sire progeny). The former is an animal that with regularity sires females that produce more milk, or perhaps more butter-fat, than their dams, and progeny that possess the type or conformation that is sought. The number of such males is limited and frequently their qualities are not recognized until after they have passed their physical prime. With young males it is only possible to speculate on the potential from knowledge of their parents and other near relations. The British Goat Society, by its method of awarding distinguishing marks to males which have sired goats, or are from dams which have given defined minimum yields, has provided guide lines which are helpful (see Appendix).

Another possibility that may be considered is line breeding or even in-breeding. Both involve restricting the choice of male to a relation of the female. When the relationship is as close as dam to son, or half sister to half brother it is known as in-breeding and when the relationship is more distant such as granddaughter to grandfather, or goats having a common grandsire, it is referred to as line breeding. This tends to fix more quickly any good points possessed: it is, however, a two-edged weapon and a process that may also perpetuate any existing weaknesses.

Some will judge a male solely on what he produces and ignore his physical attributes. Others believe that 'like begets like' and that any physical defects not appearing in the progeny may recur in subsequent generations if no effort is made to eliminate them.

For stock free from major faults, the line-bred proven sire of good physical appearance is as near as it is possible to get to the ideal.

For the owner who is concerned only with bringing about a pregnancy to freshen the milk supply and who will destroy the kids at birth, the task is much easier; any male of proved fertility can be used.

The male is normally larger than the female; weights may be 20 to 30 per cent more than for females of the same breed; height at shoulder may range from 30 inches to 38 inches.

Of the external sexual organs the testicles should be well developed, hung high and level. There is a degree of infertility in males – the main causes are stated in chapters 2 and 10. Because of this danger, the fertility of a male kid should be tested at the earliest opportunity and three or four services should be allowed around the age of six to eight months. (A healthy adult male is capable of making up to a hundred successful services in a season if these are spread evenly and he is not called upon to make more than two or three in one day.) When purchasing a male kid before it is proved, it is wise to request a written guarantee that the purchase money will be refunded in the event of its proving sterile.

The male goat emits a smell which develops at puberty, is stronger in and around the breeding season and normally remains with the animal for life. It disappears if the animal is castrated. It is thought to come from fatty glands mainly between the horns and on the neck which enlarge during the breeding season, and may be accentuated by the male's objectionable habit of frequently spraying urine and sperm over the head, chest and forelegs. As a result of this, the hair and skin become impregnated and it is almost impossible to keep these parts clean. It has recently been stated in the U.S.A. that the musk glands situated immediately behind and towards the inside of the horns, or corresponding bumps on a hornless goat, can be destroyed at birth by applying a red-hot iron in much the same way as when disbudding and that subsequently little smell develops. It will be interesting to see if this technique is developed successfully. The public has only to experience this strong and penetrating odour to associate it with all goats whereas it is only the males which have this smell. It can, however, be absorbed in the clothes of the attendant, by the building in which the goat is housed, and by milk if it is brought into close proximity. A long, plastic mackintosh kept solely for wear when handling the male is a very useful acquisition.

The need for separate housing for the male from about the age of three months is referred to on p. 53. As the male will receive less freedom than the females, an exercise yard is desirable and the housing should be adequate.

The male kid should be taught not to buck or rear as these habits can become dangerous. Satisfactory results can be obtained only by kindness and firmness. A collar or headstall, with ring attached, should always be worn and a bullstick may be used. A bullstick is a strong, wooden pole such as a long fork handle, about five to six feet long with a spring hook at one end. This spring hook can be snapped on to the ring in the goat's collar and the goat can then be held at pole's length. This will prevent the male from rubbing against or butting the attendant. The beard is a useful handhold in an emergency!

The more freedom and exercise the male can be given within sight of other goats (but not *with* them), the easier he will be to handle, and views of the outside world from his house or exercising yard will lessen his boredom. Although the task may be unpleasant, the feet must not be neglected and the usual hoof trimming must be carried out.

On warm days during the summer the male can be thoroughly washed with soft soap or detergent, but this is inadvisable at other times. It may also be necessary to grease the forelegs. The skin of an ageing male goat often tends to harden with a resultant loss of coat. To counteract this, increase the supply of greenfood, wash the affected parts daily and apply a mixture of three parts olive oil to one part surgical spirit. If a fibre doormat or a brush with short, hard bristles is firmly attached to the side of the house or yard at an appropriate height the goat will rub against this and it may help to stimulate the skin.

A male should be reared and fed well as a kid so as to obtain maximum development before breeding commences. Whilst excessive fat should be avoided, it is much more likely that difficulty will be experienced in maintaining satisfactory condition during the breeding season, when males tend to lose their appetite and eat very little. From 1 lb. to 2 lb. of concentrated food should therefore be given daily prior to and during the season, and a wide variety is desirable when the appetite is low.

Feeding in general can follow that recommended for females, bearing in mind the importance of greenfood when stall feeding is practised, and also the difference in body weight. Mangolds, sugar beet and sugar beet pulp are foods that should not be fed to males as they can cause urination troubles; swedes and carrots can be fed instead.

CHAPTER 8
Breeding

Kids of both sexes, but more particularly the male, will sometimes breed from the age of ten to twelve weeks, and will, in the appropriate season, almost always breed from the age of six months. In consequence, the sexes should be separated from the age of three months.

In tropical and semi-tropical countries the goat will often breed twice a year. In temperate countries it will not and there is a distinct breeding season, although the odd mating may occur at any time. Records of over 6,000 fertile matings in Britain showed that the percentage made in each month was as follows:

January	5.6%	July	1.4%
February	3.6%	August	4.9%
March	2.7%	September	15.1%
April	1.0%	October	28.4%
May	.4%	November	24.4%
June	.6%	December	11.9%

Thus 79.8 per cent took place in the months of September to December inclusive, and 90.3 per cent between August and January inclusive. The females are usually unready to mate, or else fail to mate successfully, at other times. The breeding season is associated with lessening hours of daylight, thus in Australia the height of the season is in April and May.

It is customary in Britain to delay mating the female until it is about eighteen months old, whereas in most other countries it is the practice to breed at six to nine months. When bred in the first autumn, growth is undoubtedly retarded and may then not be completed until the third or fourth year. The delayed breeding and a higher nutritional scale may have jointly contributed to the goats in Britain being larger than elsewhere, but there is little evidence that earlier breeding has any detrimental effect on eventual size or milk production.

The practice in Britain has been to breed goats annually with the intention of obtaining maximum milk production and young stock but several reasons account for a growing tendency to breed less regularly (in perhaps two years out of three). The first reason is that with goats capable of high yields, the lactation can be extended readily to two years or more (see chapter 11) with perhaps no loss in overall milk production over the period and fewer milk gluts and shortages that tend to occur with a limited breeding season and the desirability of a 'dry' period prior to kidding. The other reasons are the limited demand for kids and the fact that less breeding will minimize the strains of pregnancy. It can however, be difficult to get an older goat in kid when wanted after a lactation of eighteen months or more.

A goat is said to be 'in season' or 'on heat' when oestrus occurs and it is ready to accept the male. This condition is most likely to first occur in September or October and to recur at three-week intervals until mating and conception takes place, or the breeding season terminates. It is readily noticed for the goat is very restless, bleats almost constantly, twitches its tail vigorously and there is a swelling of the vulva (the entrance to the female genital organs) from which there is often a slight discharge of a clear liquid.

It is no use trying to secure a mating if the female is not in season, although the presence of a male, or even a rag with the smell of a male, will sometimes induce season.

In spring and in summer the condition may not last for more than an hour or so and be detected only by the presence of a male goat. In the height of the breeding season it normally lasts two to three days. The mating should take place while the manifestations are strong – about the middle of that period. When an owner does not possess a male goat or if there is any uncertainty as to whether a goat is in season or not it may be desirable, in view of the limited time available, to make all the necessary arrangements for service to take place when the goat is in season again three weeks later.

If a goat does not come in season by December the novice should seek the advice of an experienced breeder or a vet.

Few goat owners with less than four or five females keep a male goat. They find it more pleasant, convenient and cheaper to transport the female to the nearest suitable male. Occasionally the male-goat owner is prepared to take the male to the female. While this involves transport costs, over and above a stud fee which in Britain may vary from £1 to £4 or £5, it avoids the necessity of purchasing and maintaining a male. With six or more females to mate, the breeder normally owns a male which is then made available to other goat owners, the stud fees received contributing to the cost of maintenance. Where accommodation is available a stud-goat owner will often board a female for a period during which it is expected to come in season, at a charge of around £1.50 to £2 a week, and this can avoid fruitless journeys.

Much work on the artificial insemination of goats has been carried out in Canada by the Ontario Veterinary College, from which frozen semen has been exported to America, Germany and the Netherlands, with a conception rate varying from 70 to 80 per cent.

In some countries, notably Russia and France, breeding by this means has been carried out on an extensive scale, but in Britain the demand for it has been minimal and regulations covering a procedure for the registration of kids bred by artificial insemination, adopted in 1946, have only once been used.

Skills are required in connection with the collection, preservation and implantation of the semen and unless greater interest develops, costs are likely to prevent this method of breeding becoming readily available to goat-keepers in Britain.

When a male and female are placed together for mating it should be in an enclosed yard and ideally neither should be tied, fastened, or held in any way. They should be left alone but watched to make sure that mating takes place. With a vigorous adult male it may be difficult to get the female away and some breeders prefer to hold the female by the collar to facilitate quick removal after mating. If the male is willing but the female is not it is probably due to the fact that she is not properly in season and it is useless to persist.

Some breeders seek a second service on the same day but this should not be necessary and it may place a strain on a male in a busy breeding season.

A stud-goat owner should issue a certificate of service stating the name and registered number of both the male and female and the date of service, as this will be required in connection with registration of the progeny. It will also serve as a receipt for the stud fee which is payable in advance. If the first service is unsuccessful it is customary to allow a second service, three weeks later, free of charge.

Watch carefully three weeks after service for any signs of the goat coming in season again. If this occurs it must be assumed that the goat is not in kid and arrangements be made for a further service. If there are no such signs it is reasonable to hope that the first mating was successful. There is no simple method of confirming hopes and sometimes an experienced goat-keeper is mistaken, but six weeks or so before the expected date of birth there is usually evidence in the shape and size of the body, the milk yield or lack of it, and visible movements in the body which can be attributed to the developing kid or kids and are often more noticeable when the goat is drinking.

If there are any signs of worm infestation take action early in pregnancy or delay it until after the goat has kidded (see p. 77). The goat should have adequate exercise during pregnancy and should be forced to exercise in the later stages, if she is unwilling.

Milk yield during pregnancy is unpredictable. An increase for a few weeks may follow mating, after which it is normal for it to decline steadily until the goat is dry about six weeks prior to kidding. If there is no sign of drying off this should be encouraged by failing to strip after each milking, by irregular milking or by milking once daily. If this action fails, as it may if the yield is high, it is better to accept defeat. If normal milking is resumed there will be no colostrum at the time of kidding (see p. 65).

Goatlings, in particular, may develop milk in association with the impending kidding as much as weeks or only hours before the event takes place. Again it is necessary to watch and wait and only if the udder is unduly stretched, hot and inflamed, should small quantities of milk be drawn off from time to time.

A goat or goatling in kid has additional nutritional needs which increase, particularly after the first two months. The animal's reserves must also be built up to meet the strain imposed by heavy yield in the three or four months after giving birth. Best results are achieved by additional concentrates and good hay rather than by increasing the succulents. Up to 1 lb. of concentrates and 2 lb. of hay in addition to the allowances quoted on p. 46 should be given during the last three months of pregnancy.

The period of gestation is five months or one hundred and fifty days. There are exceptions, and extremes of 136 days and 157 days have been noted. The most frequent variants are a day or two less than the normal. The following abbreviated table is given for handy reference:

Mating Date	Kidding Date	Mating Date	Kidding Date
Jan. 1	May 31	July 16	Dec. 13
Jan. 15	June 14	July 30	Dec. 27
Jan. 29	June 28	Aug. 13	Jan. 10
Feb. 12	July 12	Aug. 27	Jan. 24
Feb. 26	July 26	Sept. 10	Feb. 7
Mar. 12	Aug. 9	Sept. 24	Feb. 21
Mar. 26	Aug. 23	Oct. 8	Mar. 7
Apr. 9	Sept. 6	Oct. 22	Mar. 21
Apr. 23	Sept. 20	Nov. 5	Apr. 4
May 7	Oct. 4	Nov. 19	Apr. 18
May 21	Oct. 18	Dec. 3	May 2
June 4	Nov. 1	Dec. 17	May 16
June 18	Nov. 15	Dec. 31	May 30
July 2	Nov. 29		

Be prepared for the kidding several days before the due date. A disinfected loose box, free of pails or other obstructions and well bedded down, is required. The goat should not be tied up.

Signs of the imminence of kidding, which may appear two or three hours in advance, are apprehension, restlessness and discomfort – a tendency to scratch frequently at the bedding, to lie down and rise again, and to bleat more than usual. The udder will fill up rapidly. The position of the kid or kids will have moved and cavities or hollows are likely to appear in the flanks and on each side of the tail. The vulva will widen. A discharge may commence a few days earlier but it is more likely to appear at this stage and when it changes in appearance from a thick white opaque substance to a slimy mucus and the water bag begins to appear, kidding is imminent.

It must be emphasized that this is a normal process and nine times out of ten passes off without the slightest complication and without any need for human aid. Wrongly presented kids, a particularly large kid or the presence of a dead kid are complications that sometimes occur.

In view of the slight risk of such complications, owners of pedigree stock like to try and be present at the birth and to that end may visit the goat once or twice during the night if kidding is thought to be imminent. As often as not, such surveillance is unsuccessful and the kids are found frisking around their dam in her loose box, or perhaps in the paddock if born during the day.

The correct presentation is for the two forefeet to appear together with the nose of the kid lying on the forelegs and with these in sight there is rarely any problem or delay although straining may continue for five or ten minutes before the whole of the head appears and the kid is delivered. With this correct presentation it is possible to assist delivery, if necessary, by pulling the forelegs in a downwards direction in unison with the straining. While normal delivery takes place with the goat lying down, it can equally well take place standing. One cannot know how many kids to expect or how soon after one another they will appear – an interval of between fifteen and twenty minutes is common. A second kid is sometimes presented, quite successfully, hind legs first. Delivery of a second or third kid is usually easier than the first.

The attendant should watch without fussing or disturbing the goat, only intervening if there are signs that all is not well. Those signs will be if, after frequent straining for say an hour there is no sign at all of a kid, or half an hour after the forefeet are in view, there is no progress.

A novice should call in the aid of a vet, or someone with appropriate experience, to ascertain and correct any form of wrongful presentation before attempting such a task personally. It involves inserting a hand and arm into the vagina and uterus for a manual exploration, preferably with the goat standing. Absolute cleanliness is essential; the finger nails should be cut short and after washing with an appropriate disinfectant the hand and forearm should be lubricated with soap immediately before insertion. If the goat appears unwell the next day, an injection of penicillin will often counteract any infection.

The water bag in which the kid is contained prior to birth will break internally and the liquid it contains lubricate the vagina: it should not be interfered with by hand. Finally the water bag or 'afterbirth' – the protective tissues which have surrounded the foetus in the womb – will be discharged. There will be one for each kid. It is important that these should be cleared entirely within a maximum period of twelve hours failing which the assistance of a vet should be secured immediately. Retention of the afterbirth is more likely after an assisted birth, and may easily lead to infection. It is preferable to remove the afterbirths as they are dropped, but if the goat should eat one or part of one that is perfectly natural.

Finally the rear quarters of the goat can be lightly washed down with warm water and dried. A warm, oatmeal gruel drink, a bran mash (see p. 72) or some of her own colostrum is likely to be appreciated. There should be a slight sticky reddish discharge for two or three weeks after kidding: this is normal, and only calls for periodic cleansing.

The chances that when a goat kids it will have twins are slightly better than even; if it does not, the chances favour a single kid rather than triplets, but the latter are common also. The record number at one birth is six.

CHAPTER 9
Rearing

There is, in Britain, a limited demand for kids, and at birth, a decision should be made as to whether a kid is wanted as a potential replacement in the herd or whether there is likely to be a ready sale for it either then or at a later date. The fact must be faced that unless the kids are from prize-winning or equally good stock it is often impossible to rear female kids and almost invariably impossible to rear male kids and subsequently sell them at a price which will cover the cost of rearing. This cost will depend upon what alternative outlets there may be for the milk that would be consumed and there is always the possibility of rearing kids for slaughter for meat. Many breeders prefer to slaughter unwanted kids at birth, before expense has been incurred, and there should be ruthless culling to discard weakly kids and those possessing poor physical qualities.

Within a few hours of birth check each kid to ascertain (a) its sex and that the visible sexual organs appear normal, (b) whether it is naturally hornless or will develop horns, (c) whether it is free from supernumerary or malformed teats and (d) whether, if of a specific breed, it conforms to breed type. All these factors may have a bearing on whether to rear or not.

The possibility of hermaphroditism, associated with breeding for hornlessness, was referred to in chapter 2. The majority of hermaphrodites are genetically female but become intersexed during their embryonic development. The most frequent external abnormality, often visible at birth in what otherwise appears to be a female, is an enlarged clitoris, a rudimentary male sexual organ, within the lower lips of the vulva. The clitoris is seen then as a bulbous swelling about the size of a pea. Other types of hermaphroditism exist, some involving sterility in the male, but these are not often detectable at birth. While the percentage of hermaphrodites born in Britain may at one time have reached 6 or 7 per cent,

This picture shows a kid with an enlarged clitoris at the lower end of the vulva, which usually indicates that it is an hermaphrodite.

the present tendency to breed from goats that have at least one naturally horned animal in the recent pedigree is reducing that figure.

To determine whether a kid is naturally hornless it is necessary to examine the top of the head carefully to find out if, over the positions where the horn buds might be expected, there are twirls of hair growing in corkscrew fashion. If there are and that hair is parted, a small bare patch of skin, little larger than a pin head, will be revealed and those are the points from which the horns will develop. The hair on the head of a kid that is naturally hornless will point uniformly outwards from the crown or central 'rose'. Disbudding is discussed in chapter 4.

Supernumerary teats are found occasionally and can be hereditary. Such a teat if 'blind' and away from other teats should be removed as soon as possible by means of a ligature; it can also be removed using sterile scissors. If it possesses an orifice or if one of the teats is a double teat, with two orifices the kid should not be reared. A male kid should possess two rudimentary teats, one on each side of the testicles, and these too should be checked to ensure that they are normal.

Ears are sometimes bent at birth, due to folding in the womb, but these usually right themselves. Adhesive tape applied in a manner to correct the shape, is sometimes helpful. When it is decided to rear, paint what remains of the navel cord with tincture of iodine to reduce danger of infection through that channel.

Unwanted kids should be destroyed in a humane manner at birth. The use of a captive bolt pistol or chloroform is recommended. For the former hold the left ear of the kid in the left hand and place the pistol against the centre of the back of the head just above an imaginary line drawn between the posterior edges of the ears and below a bone prominence that can be felt, and fire the bolt in line between that point and the kid's muzzle. In Britain a £3.50 Fire Arms Licence must be applied for and be granted by the police to hold a captive bolt pistol, which should be kept, together with any anaesthetics, under lock and key at all times. With chloroform place about 2 oz. on a pad of cotton wool in the bottom of a wide-mouthed 2 lb. jam jar. With the kid on a table or bench, its head should be held lightly in the mouth of the jar until it becomes anaesthetized and the body goes limp, which should occur within a few minutes. The jar should then

In this picture, the female kid has a false teat attached to a normal teat. If the false teat does not possess an orifice, it can be satisfactorily removed.

be pushed right over the head and left in that position, so that only chloroform is breathed, for about half an hour. The ideal method of destruction is by the injection of a suitable drug using a hypodermic syringe, but this should be done only by a veterinary surgeon or on his instructions.

The choice of rearing methods rests between the natural method by which the dam suckles the young and the artificial method by which the kid or kids are separated from their dam and hand reared on a bottle or by means of a pail or some similar method.

The natural method is labour-saving and provided the dam has sufficient milk is satisfactory for the kid, which receives its milk as and when required and at the right temperature. It is far less satisfactory if the dam and her milk production are prior considerations. There are, under the natural system, no means by which the yield of the dam can be accurately measured and, if the yield is heavy, milk may not be drawn evenly from both halves of the udder, with the danger of an uneven udder resulting. It will still be necessary to strip the dam twice a day to ensure maximum yield. With hand rearing the quantity of milk can be regulated or it can be diluted as desired and the kid can be sold at any time without a weaning process. Those that are hand reared are always less timid and easier to handle.

Goat owners with pedigree stock almost invariably employ the hand-rearing method and prefer bottle feeding, or a similar method, to pan or pail feeding. Taking the milk from a teat is nearer to nature and ensures that the milk is swallowed with saliva at a lower rate than when drunk from a pail. This is advantageous to the digestive system and thought to justify the more laborious method.

Kids that are to be hand-reared should be removed from their dams after three or four days. If the dam is taken from the goat house and the kids are removed out of earshot during her absence they will scarcely be missed, but if taken directly from her presence she is more likely to fret. If removed at such an early age the kids will not attempt to suckle their dams after a week's enforced separation.

The success of bottle feeding is dependent upon the suitability, quantity and regularity of the feeds, the absolute cleanliness of the utensils used and feeding at blood heat.

In the early stages, four feeds a day are suitable. A small glass bottle of the type containing mineral water, with a soft rubber teat or a solid plug-type teat with a vent, is most suitable. If the dam is still making the abnormal milk, produced after giving birth, known as colostrum which contains antibodies and has a laxative effect, it should be used. As it tends to curdle when heated, it can be drawn from the dam as required, using pre-warmed receptacles. A proprietary iodized mineral powder can be added, say half a teaspoonful in one feed a day, from two weeks. At three to four weeks the small bottle can be changed for a larger one with a capacity of one and a quarter pints (approximately the size of a wine bottle but must be of white glass), with a stout calf teat. As such a bottle has no vent to allow air to replace the milk sucked out, a small hole can be drilled through the shoulder of the bottle and that side kept uppermost. Alternatively a suitable receptacle such as a short, stainless steel trough or a large, glass container with two or more outlets fitted with teats can be fixed in such a way that a number of kids can be fed at once.

Starting at around a pint a day, the quantity of milk can be steadily increased to three pints by the age of four weeks and need never go higher, as the kid should then be eating some solid food. Four pints of milk feed a day and one and a half pints at any one feed should be maximums at any time. From the digestive angle, it is best to only just satisfy the appetite. If scouring – a form of diarrhoea – develops, some failure in feeding methods should be suspected and the likely cause be eliminated before looking for other possible reasons. As an antidote dilute the milk with 50 per cent water and then add a teaspoonful of powdered chalk.

One month is also the age at which the introduction of a milk substitute or skim milk can be considered if the milk is urgently required for other purposes. It should be gradually introduced over a period of ten days or so.

Usually four feeds a day will be reduced to three at eight to ten weeks, to two at say sixteen weeks and one feed a day be continued to the age of six months. On the other hand leading exhibitors are likely to continue four feeds to between three and four months, three a day to six months and continue with one a day to nine months or a year.

Where it is necessary to reduce costs and labour to the barest minimum, kids are weaned from their dams at the age of eight to ten weeks. This is best achieved by first shutting the kids away at night and eventually allowing them access to their dams for a short period only after each milking, having left some milk in the udder for their consumption. It will be necessary to keep them away from their dams for at least a month before they can be relied upon not to suckle if given the opportunity.

Kids should be encouraged to eat solids from the age of a week or so when they will begin to nibble greenfood, hay,

A British Toggenburg goatling, aged eighteen months, and winner of many prizes; well grown and developed and possessing what is described as 'quality'. Owner and breeder: Mrs. J. Paine.

coarse concentrate meals specially prepared for young stock or even the earth thrown up on a mole-hill! It is wise to introduce as many foods as possible in the first year avoiding only those with an excessive fibre content (brushwood, gorse etc.) and feeding nuts of a size which can be swallowed whole. Quantities of concentrates can vary from ¼ lb. daily for kids two or three months old to 1 lb. daily for goatlings. Growth rate and condition are the best guides as to whether the amount fed is excessive or too little. Excessive fat is as undesirable as lack of condition. Greenfood, hay and other roughages are perhaps of more importance than concentrates. An adequate supply of solid food is just as important as a plentiful supply of milk. When weaned, water should always be available.

In order to reduce labour, house all female kids in one loose box and all goatlings in another. Bedding should be clean and dry. Sunlight and exercise are necessary. Hand-reared kids will be old enough to go out with the herd from a month upwards if the weather is fine and warm. Under no circumstances should kids be tethered. Young stock should be handled frequently and from about two months be taught to lead with the use of a light collar and lead or chain.

It is not unusual for goatlings, or even kids, to develop milk before they have been mated. This is not necessarily a sign they will develop into exceptional milkers and, as it places a further demand upon the growing animal, should not be encouraged. The situation must be watched and if the udder or teats become very tight or inflamed some but not all of the milk should be drawn off. The udder may develop unevenly, making it necessary, by massaging, to try and encourage milk to develop in the smaller side, and thus even it up. Undesirable as it may be, it is better to milk regularly rather than let udder troubles develop.

The weight of a normal kid at birth may range from 4½ lb. to 11½ lb., dependent in part upon whether it is a 'singleton', one of a pair or one of triplets, and also upon whether it is a male or female. A male usually weighs about ¾ lb. more than a female and may show a growth rate of as much as 5 lb. per week in the early stages. The following growth rate figures are the average of all females (over fifty in number) born in one herd over a period of eight years and indicate what may be expected.

Age	Weight	Average Weekly Gain
At birth	8¼ lb.	–
1 month	21 lb.	3.19 lb.
2 months	32 lb.	2.75 lb.
4 months	57 lb.	3.12 lb.
6 months	73 lb.	2.00 lb.
12 months	108 lb.	1.50 lb.
18 months	136½ lb.	1.16 lb.
21 months	144 lb.	0.64 lb.

It will not be difficult for breeders to produce higher figures, but these are representative for females that will weigh about 150 lb. as adults.

CHAPTER 10
Illness and Treatment

The goat is a very healthy animal under normal conditions and sickness, when it is experienced, can often be attributed to faults in management or forcing methods designed to achieve abnormal results.

The ability to observe quickly the first symptoms of ill health is most important. The condition of the flesh and coat, appetite, alertness, nature of the droppings, failure to chew the cud and fluctuations in milk yield should be observed from day to day as they often give the first indication of illness. Other symptoms that may be noted are a distended body, signs of anaemia, or pain, lameness, or a cough.

When in doubt checks can be made on temperature, pulse and respiration. Normal temperature ranges between 102.5° and 103° F. (39° C.), the pulse rate between 70 and 80, and the rate of respiration between 22 and 26 to the minute. With a temperature of 105° F. the pulse rate may go up to 120 per minute.

Temperature is taken by placing the thermometer, which has been smeared with liquid paraffin, with a rotating movement, in the rectum, pulse should be taken where it is possible to lay the fingers gently on a main artery where it overlays bone, such as high up in the thigh or below the jaw, and respiration can be noted by watching the flank with the goat lying down.

A high temperature indicates a fever and a low or subnormal one a state of collapse. Irregularity in the pulse beat suggests a heart weakness, and abnormal respiration congestion in the chest or lungs.

Successful diagnosis calls for an understanding of the symptoms and a knowledge of the illnesses they indicate. Some symptoms, however, are common to several quite distinct diseases, and treatment without sufficient knowledge can be dangerous.

The experienced breeder may have the necessary knowledge to diagnose correctly and apply appropriate treatment, but will not have the professional training, or the latest information or the laboratory facilities available to the veterinary surgeon. There should be *no* hesitation in seeking professional assistance where any doubts exist or the necessary treatment cannot be provided readily by a goat-keeper.

Some illnesses and accidents occur with alarming suddenness and the owner should be in a position to take the correct remedial action without delay.

The keeping of all appropriate articles and materials in one place, preferably in a medicine chest, will save valuable time in an emergency. It is debatable what the contents of this chest should be and they will undoubtedly increase with the size of the herd and the experience of the owner, but the following can be regarded as basic:

Dettol or similar disinfectant
Surgical gauze and cotton wool
Elastoplast bandages (2 in.)
Bowl, soap and towel
Scissors (with rounded ends)
Drenching bottle
Worming tablets or powders
Gaseous fluid (proprietary liquid designed to combat flatulence or indigestion)
Enema syringe
Measuring glass
Clinical thermometer
Medicinal paraffin
Epsom salts
Bicarbonate of Soda
Flowers of Sulphur
Udder salve
Embrocation or liniment
Kaolin or powdered chalk
Golden eye ointment or eye drops
Parrish's Food

Some experience of giving injections should be gained before one or more 10 c.c. plastic disposable hypodermic syringes with needles and some of the injections they would be used for, are included.

When an animal is ill it appreciates warmth. This can be provided by a well-littered draught-free box and a fitted coat or rug: an overhead infra-red electric heater is an added refinement. Sunlight, fresh air and quietness are often helpful.

Today professional treatment leans towards injections and tablets, but drenching is still often called for as a first-aid measure. A half-pint beer bottle will serve for an adult or a smaller one of similar shape for a kid. With the goat in a corner, its mouth must be held open with the left hand and with the right hand the drenching bottle should be inserted in the side of the mouth. The bottle must be tilted slightly above the horizontal to ensure that the drench trickles slowly down the throat, for if it is held higher there is a danger of the fluid entering the windpipe and the lungs, with the sub-

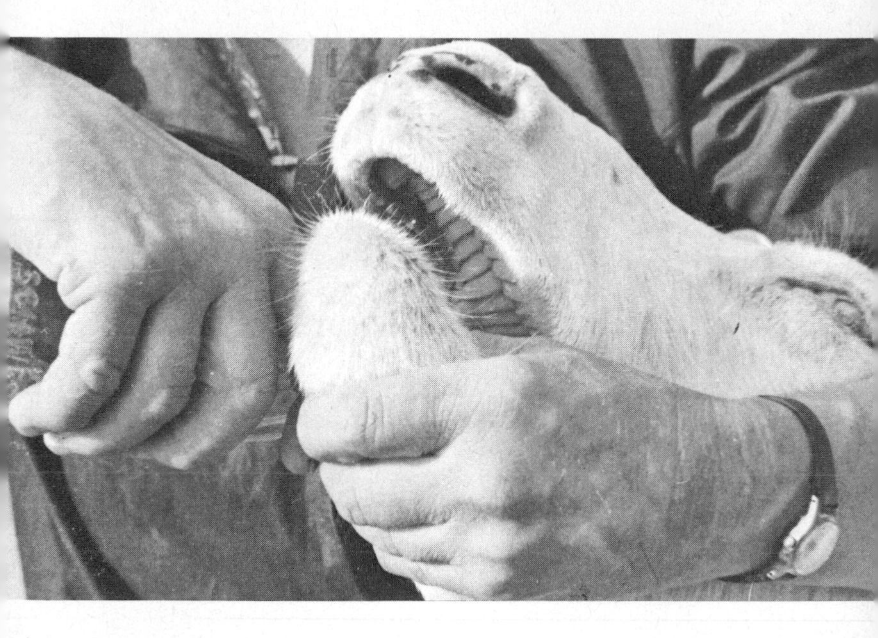

Drenching, showing the way in which the mouth is held open with the left hand and the angle at which the drenching bottle should be held with the right hand.

sequent possibility of pneumonia. If the roof of the mouth is touched with the bottle before pouring commences this will encourage the goat to close its windpipe. When administering tablets or powders these should be placed as far back as possible on the tongue, the muzzle should be held closed and the gullet under the jaw stroked to encourage the goat to swallow.

If appetite is lost, a day or so without food is seldom harmful, but beyond this food is essential. Consequently the goat must be tempted to eat by offering as great a variety of food as possible. When a goat refuses the normal concentrate mixtures a bran mash or linseed tea can be tried – both have a slightly laxative effect. A bran mash is made by pouring over a half pail of bran as much boiling water as it will readily absorb and then covering the pail to retain the heat and steam: it should be fed an hour later when it has cooled. Linseed tea is prepared by bringing ½ lb. of crushed linseed slowly to the boil in half a gallon of water and allowing it to simmer at near boiling point for six to eight hours, when it can be poured over any light, bulky, dry food or drunk from a pail. Another alternative is oatmeal gruel, made by adding sufficient fine oatmeal to boiling water in an open pan and stirring continuously until the desired consistency is reached. Milk can also be offered. The forcible feeding of slops should only be attempted as a last resource. Parrish's Food is a time-honoured and useful tonic in cases of debility. It contains phosphates of iron, calcium, potassium and sodium. A tablespoonful for an adult or two teaspoonfuls for a kid, administered three times daily in a little water, is the correct dosage.

Keep a goat propped up with sacks of straw rather than allow it to lie flat and encourage it to use its legs when it is capable of doing so. Keeping a goat on its feet by means of a sling is not recommended except under special circumstances.

Careful nursing is necessary, for goats cannot be described as good patients. When seriously ill they often appear to lack the will to live, they are not good subjects for anaesthesia by ether or chloroform and sulphanilamide is highly toxic for the goat.

The following accidents, conditions or diseases may occur suddenly:

(a) *Accidents.* The most common accident is the tearing of the udder in a hedge or on barbed wire. If the tear is extensive and likely to require stitching the vet should be called, and he may also decide to give an anti-tetanus injection. Minor wounds should be cleansed of all foreign substances with a mild disinfectant. A dry dressing of gauze and cotton wool should then be applied and held in place with elastoplast. If the tear is anywhere other than on the udder or teat first clip the hair away from the affected area. The breakage of a limb is a rare occurence; the goat should be kept still and professional advice be sought.

(b) *Poisoning.* Various plants are poisonous but in the main these are ignored by the goat or eaten in innocuous quantity. The degree of toxicity varies from plant to plant, with the time of year and the quantity eaten; some goats seem to be able to eat with impunity, substances to which others react. There are, however, two highly poisonous shrubs – rhododendron and yew – which goats will often eat and to which they must be denied access.

The symptoms of rhododendron and yew poisoning are broadly the same – profuse diarrhoea, salivation, dullness, straining, abdominal pain and unsteady gait. After eating yew, sudden collapse may occur at any time, while rhododendron poisoning causes vomiting which is most unusual in a ruminant. Professional aid must be sought. First aid must consist of a purge to pass the poison through the system as quickly as possible. A teaspoonful of bicarbonate of soda mixed in a tablespoonful of melted lard will serve and should be followed by stimulants to counteract shock. Black coffee, or 1 oz. of whisky or brandy in 4 oz. of water, can be given at two to three hour intervals.

Some milder forms of poisoning can have an accumulative effect. These include not only plant poisoning but chemical poisoning resulting from the use of toxic sprays, rat poison, and chemical reaction on such metals as lead and copper when used as food or water containers, or through the use of lead paint. Linseed cake exposed to the weather, and frozen greens can also develop toxic properties.

(c) *Hoven or Blown.* An acute form of indigestion which may develop quickly when, as the result of eating an excessive quantity of succulent food, gases develop in the stomach, and it becomes necessary to take remedial action. Symptoms are a distended body, particularly on the left flank, where the skin may become drum-tight, with signs of discomfort and pain. Drenching with a proprietary gaseous fluid, vigorous massage of the body with the goat's forefeet raised on a box, and exercise, may bring the desired relief, failing which it is sometimes necessary to release the gas by puncturing the flank with a trocar – a task for a vet.

(d) *Entero-Toxaemia.* A disease so acute that a goat may be found dead without having displayed any symptoms. It is experienced mainly in goatlings and goats in high condition following a sudden change of diet, such as the introduction of succulent greenfood in quantity. The cause is an organism known as Clostridium Welchii type D, which is often present inactively in the intestines and harmless until some particular circumstances (of which little are known) activate it and a highly poisonous toxin is formed. Symptoms include a sudden drop in milk yield, loss of appetite, staggering gait, severe diarrhoea (sometimes bloodstained), and persistent and compulsive straining. Death often takes place within a matter of hours. Treatment involves injections by a vet, and there is some chance of recovery in less acute attacks. When the disease is experienced, the herd should be vaccinated against it, but the immunity given will only be temporary.

(e) *Mastitis.* This term is a generalization for inflammation of the udder which may be brought about by a number of causes, but in particular it is used for both acute and milder forms of inflammation caused by bacterial infection. It is customary for milk, when drawn from a mammal, to carry some bacteria, and it is when this normality is exceeded by a considerably degree that trouble develops. In the acute form, which is seldom experienced in goats, there is heat, swelling and pain in the udder and obviously abnormal milk is produced; it is possible for part of the udder to slough off. It is the milder forms that are more insidious for the symptoms are not always recognized: they include the thickening of the milk on heating or standing, and the presence of flakes, curds or clots in the milk which may possess a salty flavour. Lumps may gradually appear in the udder, as a result of damage to the glandular tissues.

Veterinary assistance should be sought when the disease is suspected for the milk must be tested and treatment, probably in the form of penicillin injections through the teat, will depend upon the type of infection found. Early treatment may clear up the infection quickly, but if neglected it may easily become chronic.

The disease is highly infectious and carried from one goat to another by the milker's hands. A goat known to be infected should be milked last.

(f) Colic. This is an acute form of indigestion, sometimes experienced by kids, which causes extreme griping pains. It may be caused by violent exercise after a large feed of milk, and be associated with a stoppage. A 2 oz. dose of liquid paraffin may assist, and a rubber ear syringe can be used to give an enema of soap and water. The kid writhes in agony and must be restrained.

The following may be encountered in breeding:

(a) *Sterility.* The failure of a female goat to breed may be due to (i) malformation of the sexual organs, (ii) abnormalities such as cystic ovaries, a regressive *corpus lutem,* or inactive ovaries which cause the absence of or irregularity in the heat periods, (iii) infective conditions in the genital tract, sometimes, but by no means always, indicated by a persistent discharge. Failure on the part of the male may be (i) structural, (ii) functional, such as extreme youth or old age, overwork, or inability to complete intercourse, or (iii) result from damage to the genital tract, inflammation of the testicles, or inadequacy of the ejaculate, either in the activeness or the numbers of sperm.

The fertility of a male can be proved by veterinary examination of a sample of semen, but the effectiveness of the female organs cannot be checked so readily. Acidity can sometimes be countered by syringing out the vagina, about half an hour before mating, with a pint of warm water in which 1 oz. of bicarbonate of soda has been dissolved. If an apparent female develops or regularly adopts male characteristics, it may be an hermaphrodite. Professional advice is sometimes helpful, but dependent upon circumstances, it is often wise to 'cut losses' and discard the doubtful breeder.

(b) *Acetonaemia and Pregnancy Toxaemia.* These are diseases associated with metabolism and changes which tend to occur in the blood stream during pregnancy due to the strain caused by the developing foetus. General symptoms are sluggishness and depression. With acetonaemia, there is a nail-varnish smell to the milk, urine and breath, and with toxaemia the goat tends to stagger and grind its teeth and eventually becomes comatose. Veterinary treatment may comprise injections of glucose. These conditions are unlikely to occur where the carbohydrate and mineral contents of the food are high and the ration is appropriately increased in the final stages of pregnancy.

(c) *False conception or Cloud Burst.* This condition is not uncommon with goats that are not mated each year or goatlings where breeding has been delayed. After mating, or without having been mated, the goat's body increases in size and there is every appearance of it being in kid. Suddenly, and often around the date it is due to kid, up to three gallons of pale watery fluid are discharged in a matter of minutes, and the body reverts to its normal size. The condition recurs in some goats. Little is known of the precise cause and the occurrence has little bearing on the general health of the goat. An attempt to remate should not be made until the discharge which follows the 'cloud burst' has disappeared, although the goat may come in season earlier.

(d) *Abortion.* In Britain the goat does not suffer from contagious abortion or from brucellosis. A goat may expel its foetus before the due date as a result of shock, fright, fighting or similar heavy exertion and occasionally as the result of having eaten frosted roots. Treat as though the goat had kidded normally but if, as is probable, the afterbirth is retained, veterinary advice should be sought.

The goat-keeper may also encounter the following ailments and diseases:

(a) *Intestinal Parasites.* Probably the most common cause of ill health. It is customary for goats having access to grass to carry these parasites, commonly referred to as worms, in moderation and to develop some resistance to the irritation and damage they cause. Young stock, adults with health impaired by other causes and the aged are particularly susceptible to heavier infestations. Symptoms which appear only when infestation is high are lumpy droppings (developing into diarrhoea), loss of condition, staring coat and anaemia. If no action is taken, parasitic gastro-enteritis or bronchitis may develop.

There are various species of this type of parasite, found either in the fourth stomach, the small intestine or the bronchial tube, and the species which causes the greatest damage is *haemonchus contortus,* a blood sucker the ravages of which, in a heavy infestation, may be equivalent to severe daily bleedings.

Another parasite which can cause death is *coccidea,* to which young kids are often susceptible and for which adults may act as carriers. A symptom is very acute diarrhoea – confirmed by egg count (see next page).

The basic life cycle of the various species is similar. The adult worms lay eggs in the body of their host in enormous numbers and these are passed to the ground in the droppings. Under favourable conditions of moisture and warmth the eggs develop into larval forms which climb blades of grass and other vegetation which is eaten by the goat and thus re-entry into the host is gained via the mouth. The cycle may be complete in two or three weeks, but the larvae have been known to survive for a year in pasture.

Prevention is better than cure and thus the necessity to avoid constant use of small areas of grass, particularly if overstocked, cannot be over-emphasized. If land is rested for as little as six weeks it will do much to break the life cycle.

The surest way to determine whether goats are suffering from an excessive infestation is to ask a vet to send a sample of droppings for a laboratory egg-count which will reveal not only the extent to which worms are present but also the different varieties, and treatment may depend upon this factor and the degree of infestation.

Some breeders like to dose regularly as a precautionary measure but it is better to take an egg count at regular intervals followed by treatment when necessary.

There are several proprietary vermifuges which will act on most types of worms. Some are poisonous in a minor degree to the host or have side effects. New preparations are appearing frequently. The most commonly used today is 'Thibenzole' which is non-poisonous and available in tablet or powder form: two level teaspoonfuls of the powder in a cupful of water, given as a drench, is the appropriate dosage for an adult. Others are 'Mintic' and 'Frantin'. At one time 'Phenothiazine' was the recognized treatment and is certainly effective, but this tended to turn the milk and the urine pink. Sulphamezathine, in capsule form, is a recognized treatment for coccidiosis.

(b) *Pox.* Goats are subject to two types of pox, one known as goat pox, which normally affects the skin of the udder, and the other, pustular dermatitis, which more commonly attacks the lips, nose and feet. Both are contagious virus diseases and tend to spread rapidly from one goat to another unless the victims are isolated. The first symptom is reddened areas that later develop pus and a raised crust in which the virus is present and which eventually dries and falls off, the process taking about three weeks. There is no recognized treatment other than bathing with peroxide of hydrogen in an equal part of water, followed by the application of drying powders, or, if too dry, an antiseptic cream.

(c) *Retention of Urine.* Common in male goats and caused by stone in the bladder. Hot fomentations may relieve pain and drinks of barley water should be given. In serious cases involving an operation which may cause sterility, it is probably preferable to have the goat destroyed.

(d) *Rheumatism.* Sometimes experienced in the pasterns and knees. Affected joints may be swollen, hot and painful. Hot fomentations may alleviate pain and 20 gr. of sodium salycilate can be given three times daily in the food. Prevention is easier than cure and deep, dry bedding is the wisest precaution.

(e) Lice. Three species of lice may attack goats and their presence is indicated by the host biting, scratching or rubbing, but they are seldom much trouble on a goat in good health. The whole life of the parasite is spent in the coat although it can live up to a fortnight elsewhere. The eggs hatch in one to two weeks and the full life cycle lasts four to ten weeks. Dusting with flowers of sulphur sprinkled from a pepper pot, with the coat turned back and particular attention to the underparts, will normally serve as an effective control.

(f) *Blood in Milk.* Occasionally milk, when drawn, may be slightly pink in colour and show a small deposit of blood. This is the result of the rupturing of a small blood vessel in the udder. With gentle handling the trouble usually rights itself within a few days and without any specific treatment.

(g) *Sore Teats or Udder.* Sore teats cause irritation to both goat and milker and every care should be taken to avoid them. The cause may be chapping in cold weather, scratches or insect bites. The use of a good proprietory udder salve will do much to keep the udder and teats in good, soft, pliable condition.

(h) *Eye Trouble.* The eye is always a delicate organ and even minor damage to it can be painful and cause the tear duct to operate. Particles of hay falling from a rack, draughts and similar causes may result in 'pink-eye' and should be treated by the application of eye drops or golden eye ointment (1 per cent oxide of mercury in a suitable base).

Goats are subject to anthrax and foot and mouth disease (both notifiable to the police), tetanus and tuberculosis, but they are very rarely experienced. Forty years ago milk fever, goitre (enlarged thyroid glands) and rickets were prevalent but a better understanding of the needs for mineral supplements has resulted in their virtual disappearance. This is by no means a complete list but covers those illnesses and ailments the average goat-keeper meets.

CHAPTER 11
Goats' Milk and its Production

The evaluation of goats' milk is clouded by prejudice. People who dismiss goats' milk as unpalatable rarely do so with personal knowledge. The random consumer, offered the choice of hygienically produced, unlabelled samples of goats' milk and cows' milk, can seldom distinguish one from the other and many choose the goats' milk as the sample they prefer.

Many substances are present in goats' milk in variable and minute quantities. Even with the principal solid – fat – the content varies widely, it is partly an inherited factor but is also influenced by the length of lactation, the weather, the length of time between milkings and other factors. To illustrate this – thirty-four goats of various breeds and at different stages of lactation that competed in a milking competition at a leading summer show, averaged 3.55 per cent butter fat, but thirty-five similar goats competed at an indoor show a few months later and averaged 4.42 per cent. The maximum and minimum daily averages for the goats competing in those competitions was 7.36 per cent and 2.33 per cent respectively. The average of all goats officially milk recorded and yielding over 2,000 lb. in a random recorded year is a more reliable guide, for the record of each goat was derived from a number of tests taken throughout the year under more normal home conditions; the average for 101 such goats was 3.74 per cent.

The figures relative to solids other than fats are less frequently available but at a random show the average was 8.67 per cent and this figure does not fluctuate so widely.

Goats' milk can be said to contain the same substances as cows' milk and the limits of variation in the percentage of each constituent are very similar for both.

The important differences are in the size and thickness of the wall of fat globules and the texture of the curd. The fat globules in goats' milk vary from approximately one half to less than one fifth the size of those in cows milk; this is readily demonstrated by the slowness of the rise of cream in goats' milk. The curd of goats' milk is on average about 50 per cent softer than the curd of cows' milk.

While the differences referred to may have little bearing on the comparative value of the milks as food for a healthy person, they have certain advantages in the medical field. Hippocrates, 'The Father of Medicine', advised its use for several purposes. The advantages of goats' milk have been seen in cases of stomach and intestinal disorders, where ease of digestion is of paramount importance.

Goats' milk is also used in connection with the allergy diseases, particularly those associated with skin disorders. Cases are constantly being recorded where a patient could not consume cows' milk but has taken goats' milk readily and this has brought quick relief.

Some disadvantages have been suggested but cannot be substantiated. Severe anaemia in babies fed solely on goats' milk has been attributed to its low iron and copper content, but this content is no lower than in cows' milk and nutritional anaemia is not peculiar to babies fed on goats' milk. Undulant fever or *brucella melitensis* has, in the past, been carried extensively by goats' milk in Malta. In Britain neither *brucella melitensis* nor *brucella abortus* are experienced in goats although present in cow herds.

Milk is not only a highly perishable commodity but it is one in which bacteria will develop very rapidly, and which will absorb smells from the air and flavours from food consumed. Bacteria are present in small numbers when the milk is drawn and any lack of hygiene will result in rapid multiplication. Instances of absorption are the smell of the male goat and the taste of cabbage when this is fed in large quantity.

The keeping quality of milk is considerably enhanced if it is strained through a milk pad, which is subsequently discarded, and cooled immediately after it is drawn. Cooling is best achieved by passing it over the outer surface of a metal cooler through which cold water is running, or very small quantities can be cooled by standing the milk in jugs, or similar vessels of small diameter, in running or frequent changes of cold water.

Occasionally a salty flavour or an 'off' or 'goaty' flavour will develop and cannot be attributed to any of the causes mentioned above. On rare occasions it may be inherited but it is more likely to be caused by the ill health of an individual animal – perhaps a chronic form of mastitis (see p. 74). Every effort must be made to trace and eliminate the cause. The colostrum produced immediately after kidding should not be mixed with milk for sale as it frequently curdles when boiled.

While the milk production of the individual goat varies enormously, the maximum production is remarkable. The highest yielders will frequently produce their own body weight of milk within a period of ten days – in other words a goat weighing 150 lb. will yield 15 lb. of milk a day. Experiments have shown that the goat can produce rather more milk, in relationship to body weight, than the cow but that it requires a relatively higher intake of food to do so, and thus the two animals can be regarded as equally efficient. Associated with this capacity is an ability to maintain high yields over a lactation lasting two or more years, and for goatlings sometimes to produce considerable quantities of milk before they have been mated.

Production is dependent primarily upon two factors – the inherited capacity and good management, and increasing stress is being laid on the latter. It is seldom that these two factors are present in the highest degree and thus average production is probably less than half the higher range recorded. A yield of less than 7½ lb. daily, a month or two after kidding, should be regarded as unsatisfactory. While maximum daily yield is the standard by which production is often assessed, annual yield is far more important, for while one goat may maintain a peak for two or three days only, another may do so for months, and the fall in yield with the lengthening of the lactation may also vary widely. A 365-day yield of not less than 1,500 lb. should be attainable by every owner.

Normally a goat reaches its highest yield in its second or third lactation and the maximum yield of the lactation about two months after kidding with a gradual but steady drop thereafter. If not mated, a good milker will often maintain about 50 per cent of maximum during the winter months, with the yield increasing again in February and going up to 85 per cent or more of the maximum in the early summer of the second year of lactation. If mated, the goat may go dry a month or so before it is due to kid again or maintain up to 30 per cent of the original yield to the date of kidding.

Butter-fat percentage is highest shortly after kidding, falls by about 25 per cent in three months and then steadily increases again to return to the original figure towards the end of the lactation.

Having mentioned modest aims for the newcomer to goat-keeping, official British records for (a) a 365-day yield commencing October 1st in any year and (b) a 24-hour yield, recorded at a show, can be quoted for the benefit of those for whom 'the sky is the limit'.

Breed	Annual Yield	24-hour Yield
All Breeds	6,661 lb.	23 lb. 13 oz.
Anglo-Nubian	4,271 lb.	15 lb. 14 oz.
British Alpine	6,034 lb.	23 lb. 8 oz.
British Saanen	6,442 lb.	23 lb. 2 oz.
British Toggenburg	5,668 lb.	23 lb. 13 oz.
Saanen	6,284 lb.	18 lb. 13 oz.
Toggenburg	3,544 lb.	13 lb. 9 oz.
British	6,661 lb.	21 lb. 10 oz.

To keep a sense of proportion it may be added that few yields of over 5,000 lb. are recorded and that the number of goats yielding between 4,000 lb. and 5,000 lb. seldom reach double figures in any one year. Likewise, daily yields of over 18 lb. are exceptional.

The world lactation record (365 days) is held by a Saanen goat in Australia, with a yield of 6,860 lb. at 3.3 per cent butter fat.

For authenticity it is essential that yields should be recorded under supervision and the annual records in Britain, based on twice daily weighing of milk, are carried out by National Milk Records, a division of the Milk Marketing Board, which is responsible for all cow milk recording. There are at present four forms of official recording available, all of which are approved by the British Goat Society. The number and frequency of the checks vary under the different schemes and costs vary accordingly. It is possible for owners to keep their private records free of cost but official records materially increase values when selling stock or progeny.

The 24-hour records quoted are those achieved in recognized Milking Competitions at shows, held under the regulations of the British Goat Society, which has promoted such competitions since 1894.

As a guide to breeders, the Society awards distinguishing marks (see p. 100) to those goats which achieve minimum standards in such competitions, in which points are allotted for yield, butter-fat percentage and days in milk. In a similar manner it awards marks to officially recorded goats which attain specified standards in 365-day yields.

It may have been noted that while the production of milk is recorded by weight in lbs., it is customary to sell milk by measure, namely in pints, quarts and gallons. A gallon (8 pints) of milk of average quality weighs 10.32 lb., but for most purposes 10 lb. is regarded as the equivalent of 1 gallon.

CHAPTER 12
The Utilization of Goat Products and Economics of Goat-Keeping

The prospective goat-keeper may imagine that because milk is a valuable food and goats' milk has special properties there will be a ready sale for all milk produced. In fact it is often difficult to dispose of it at an economic price.

The production of cows' milk in Britain is greater than the demand for liquid milk. It is produced on a very large scale, its price is subsidized by the Government and a guaranteed market is provided by the Milk Marketing Board which disposes of surplus liquid milk for manufacturing purposes at an uneconomic price. Goats' milk does not enjoy these advantages and the fact that the goat will not breed at all times of the year presents a further difficulty in that it is not easy to maintain a regular supply as called for by many consumers.

The result is that to secure an economic price of 25 to 50 per cent over the retail price of cows' milk it is necessary for a producer to find or more often create a 'speciality' market. Given favourable circumstances, such as producing in the vicinity of a city, this can sometimes be done by an enthusiast who is prepared to approach all doctors, health-food shops, hospitals and milk retailers in the area. Buyers will be largely those whose health will benefit from the consumption of goats' milk and who may return to a cheaper commodity when an improvement in health has been achieved. Having secured a market it is then essential to maintain supplies of a uniform quality and to contend with the problems associated with delivery, except where this is undertaken by an existing retailer.

Science is evolving means of extending the keeping qualities of milk and the production of goats' milk powder takes place in the U.S.A. but the very limited scale of production makes this uneconomic in Britain.

The production of yoghourt has been successfully exploited and any seasonal demand that coincides with the summer flush production, such as for cream and ice-cream, can be helpful. In several European countries goat cheeses are produced on a considerable scale, mostly on a co-operative basis. In Britain the quantity is insufficient to establish a recognized retail market, and in general it is more economic to sell liquid milk rather than manufacture milk products.

Goat-keepers, however, like to make butter and cheese for home consumption. The process is the same as when other milk is used except that more butter-colouring is called for. Some skill and exactitude is required to achieve good results and those seeking further information are referred to a booklet entitled "Dairy Work for Goat-keepers" (see p. 108).

A goat-keeper in Britain selling milk or dairy products has to comply with the Food and Drugs Act, 1955, under which it is an offence to offer for sale any commodity which is not of the nature, substance or quantity demanded, or which has been adulterated or diluted. A high standard of hygiene is obviously most essential but the production of goats' milk does not come within the Milk and Dairies Regulations which lay down most stringent requirements governing the production of cows' milk. The National Agricultural Advisory Service, through a local office, will give guidance in connection with production, and the local government authorities are usually prepared to test the milk for quality and cleanliness on request. The would-be retailer must also beware of local bye-laws which can require planning approval before trading can be carried out from domestic premises. When quantities are small such requirements are not always enforced but the goat-milk producer should be aware of them and be ready to comply when necessary.

Simple arithmetic shows that rearing kids for sale for milk production or breeding, if carried out by the methods recommended and widely practised, will not show a profit unless the stock are of exceptionally high quality, suitable for export, when they may realize prices rather higher than those generally obtainable on the home market.

There is an increasing demand for export and this market

could undoubtedly be extended. In five years (1964–1968) 186 goats were exported from Britain to the following countries: Barbados, Brazil, Canada, Ceylon, Dominica, France, India, Ireland, Jamaica, Kenya, Malta, Mauritius, New Zealand, Nigeria, Pakistan, South Africa, Trinidad, Uganda and the United Arab Republic. Switzerland exports many more, the majority going, however, to Germany and other European countries.

The risk that is attached to rearing for export is that enquiries received are likely to be for animals of a specified age – males as soon as they are proved stock-getters and females that are in kid for the first time. The enquiries do not always coincide with the time when stock are ready and thus rearing is to some extent an act of faith! Periodic outbreaks of foot and mouth and similar diseases amongst cattle and sheep can also result in cancelled orders and frustration.

With an increasing number of immigrants accustomed to regarding kid meat as a great delicacy, the demand for milk-fed kids, particularly those ten to twelve weeks old, is steadily increasing and a price of about 28p. per pound dead weight is now obtainable. Some goat-keepers, who regard their stock as pets, are reluctant to rear for this purpose but others cannot afford to destroy unwanted kids at birth and are ready to rear provided they can be satisfied that the killing is carried out in an humane manner, perhaps on the rearer's premises.

Some goat-keepers prefer to use surplus milk for the rearing of other classes of stock, for which there is a more stable market. There is always a good demand from butchers for milk-fed calves, lambs and pigs. Expenditure has to be incurred in purchasing good quality young stock, preferably direct from a farmer, but they all thrive on goats' milk and if sold while still primarily milk-fed the transaction should show a satisfactory return.

Goats' milk is excellent, also, for rearing puppies, kittens, poultry and all classes of small livestock, and pedigree breeders often seek it out for that purpose.

Skins can be home dressed and made into satisfactory gloves, mats and so on but there is no recognized market for the few that a breeder is likely to have for disposal at any one time.

Goat droppings make excellent manure, particularly where peat has been used as a bedding material, the combination making a rich compost. One sample of goat manure, from a herd fed balanced rations and bedded on oat straw was found on analysis to contain 2.21 per cent nitrogen, 1.49 per cent phosphate and 3.07 per cent potash, the figure for potash being higher than that normally found in farmyard manure.

Can a satisfactory living be made from goat-keeping in Britain? That question is asked frequently and, while in a few isolated instances it may have been achieved, the widely accepted answer is 'no'. Whether goats can be kept profitably is a different question and dependent upon many varying circumstances. It is impossible to define costs which are so dependent upon the nature of the holding, the quantity and type of food that can be home produced and the labour available free of cost. Production and receipts from sales are equally unpredictable. If everything is to be costed and charged against the project the answer is again probably 'no', although exceptions will be found.

The most satisfactory results, from the economic angle, are likely to be obtained on a holding that is commercially viable in other directions and where spare browsing or grazing, accommodation and labour is available. The addition of goats to such an establishment will then involve comparatively little expenditure and if a market for the milk is available the profits may easily be increased.

The majority of goat-keepers are more concerned about a supply of excellent milk for the household, or the pleasure of breeding and exhibiting pedigree stock, and regard the sale of surplus production, in whatever form it may take, as a welcome contribution towards costs.

CHAPTER 13
Exhibiting

The exhibiting of goats on a competitive basis is expanding in various parts of the world. Goat shows in Britain are now more numerous and receive more entries than at any time in the past, and exhibiting as a hobby is firmly established.

The British Goat Society controls all the larger shows in Britain, now numbering about eighty each year. A show would not succeed without the Society's 'recognition' and to obtain that a number of regulations have to be complied with and all goats entered must be registered in the Herd Book, the Foundation Book, or the Supplementary Register, (see p. 12), or in the Identification Register before they are eligible to compete.

These larger shows, mostly held in conjunction with agricultural shows, and excluding male goats, are of immense publicity value; the best goats in the country are inspected by hundreds of thousands of people who would not otherwise see them or know what the modern goat looks like. They do much to dispel the popular image of a smelly, hairy, horned animal with a great propensity for butting!

The local goat clubs organize male goat shows, to which the public are seldom invited but which enable breeders to inspect the stud goats available in their area; they also organize smaller shows to encourage the beginner.

Shows are both valuable to and popular with owners. Their value lies in the opportunity for comparison of one's own stock with those of other breeders. Their popularity may well be due to the friendly meeting place they provide for talking 'shop'.

Success gives considerable satisfaction but the need to accept the judge's decision with equanimity when it differs from the owner's opinion is a chastening experience for which one must always be prepared.

Classifications are based firstly on sex and age. The two

sexes are never in competition, except perhaps for the 'best exhibit'. Females are divided into three groups – goats or goatlings that have kidded, goatlings that have not kidded, and kids. Males, because of their more limited numbers, are usually in two age groups, adults and bucklings in one, and kids in the other.

Further division is based on breed. At the larger shows efforts are made to provide separate classes for each breed although Saanens and British Saanens, and likewise Toggenburgs and British Toggenburgs, are frequently classified together. Provision for goats known as British is made in a class described as 'Any Other Variety' in which they will compete with other breeds for which no separate class is provided. At the very small shows, goats of all breeds in one age group may compete in one class, when it is necessary for the judge to assess each animal as a member of its respective breed, as is often necessary when judging for special prizes.

It is customary for the majority of goat shows to provide 24-hour milking competitions, again sometimes on a breed basis, sometimes dividing those that have kidded once from those that have kidded more than once, or those that have previously reached a specified standard from those that have not. The milk produced in these competitions is weighed, samples are tested for butter-fat content and each exhibit is awarded points for weight of milk, butter-fat percentage, and the number of days that have elapsed since the date of last kidding.

One or two leading shows in Britain do not provide classes for kids on the grounds that it is undesirable to 'push' young stock for exhibition but elsewhere these classes receive the highest entries and shows cater accordingly.

Prize money varies widely and the first prize may be anything from £5 to £1, the entry fee from £1 downwards. Only very successful exhibitors will find that prize money won will meet their direct expenses, which are mainly entry fees and transport but may include the cost of help at home while the

An Inter-breed Champion British female goat of British Toggenburg type (three of her grandparents were in the British Toggenburg Section of the Herd Book and the fourth in the British Alpine Section). The photograph shows the wedge-shaped formation when viewed from the side and excellent conformation throughout. Owner and breeder: Mrs. J. Paine.

exhibitor is at the show. A prize, however, certainly enhances the value of a goat.

The owner contemplating exhibiting for the first time is advised to do so at a local show or, if at a larger show, with the help and guidance of an experienced exhibitor, for there is a lot to learn. There are some goats that are best kept at home — those that are in very poor condition, possess bad faults of conformation or have misshapen or defective udders. On the other hand, one or two defects need not prohibit exhibiting, for the perfect animal does not exist and it is not unusual for a judge to spend as much time assessing defects as assessing good points. If in any doubt enter for a local show and you will soon learn whether your stock are likely to achieve success.

Beware of the fact that entries are likely to close a considerable time in advance of the show. Read the schedule (sometimes called the prize list) carefully and insert correctly all the information asked for on the entry form or give an explanation as to why this is not available. Be sure that the entries are received by the secretary on the specified date – to post them two or three days later is not fair on the secretary and may result in the entries being refused.

Where good management exists, only a limited amount of special preparation is called for. The aim must be to ensure that the goat is looking its best.

The first essentials are that the goat should lead well, become accustomed to standing in such a way as to show itself to the best advantage and to being handled by a stranger to examine its udder, head, feet, etc. This will not be learned overnight and may take several weeks to acquire.

The desired gloss on the coat may be encouraged by rugging up or by feeding linseed cake for a few weeks, while regular grooming and rubbing down with a wash-leather will help. It is difficult but necessary to try and ensure that both coat and skin are clean. The state of a judge's hands after an hour or two's work indicate a general failure in this respect. In warm weather a thorough wash with a detergent a few days prior to the show is desirable, but frequent washing will have a detrimental effect on the coat. Stains, particularly on a white goat, are difficult to eradicate, but brushing in powdered chalk and then brushing it out again thoroughly will help to disguise them: prevention is better than cure in this direction. If a goat is shedding its coat, as much as possible of the old coat should be removed without leaving the skin too bare. Any long hair can be trimmed discreetly, particularly in the vicinity of the udder.

Hooves should have been cut or clipped recently – last minute action may lame the animal temporarily.

The collection of the equipment needed for both exhibits and exhibitor is quite a task and a list should be prepared and added to from time to time. Those who exhibit frequently will find it useful to keep the collection of smaller items in a suitable chest.

The larger shows are likely to supply, in a marquee or tent, individual metal loose boxes, sawn wood or hurdle pens, hurdle stalls or perhaps one hurdle enclosure for all your exhibits, with or without litter. Thus the first requirement is short chains with swivels and spring hooks, by which the goats can be fastened in their stalls or to their pens, which can often be jumped. For use in the ring, a light leather lead and collar is often chosen. Some exhibitors provide their goats with coats. While water is likely to be available, the exhibitor will need to provide all food, and food and water receptacles. Milking pails, at least one for each milker, are another necessity. One or two small canvas sheets, to make good any defects in the covered accommodation are often an asset. Strong cord, a hammer, a knife, tin tacks or drawing pins are other items that will prove useful and some exhibitors provide their own wire 'fronts' to convert stalls into pens. The show papers, including the exhibit numbers, must not be forgotten.

For personal use the exhibitor, who often prefers to sleep in a spare pen in the immediate vicinity of his or her exhibits, will need to provide everything, other than the tent, which would be required for a camping week-end, remembering that it can often be cold and wet.

It is becoming the custom for exhibitors to own and drive their own transport. This may consist of a shooting brake, a fitted van big enough to accommodate all goats which are to be exhibited, or a Land Rover with a trailer. Goats travel well in this way, and provided they have room to lie down, are best contained within a limited space. A few goats in a large lorry are much more likely to be thrown about and injured.

It is best to arrive at a show at least two hours before the specified time to get settled in before the milkers are stripped for the milking competition or, in the case of young stock, before judging commences. Apart from the fact that a latecomer is often at a disadvantage, this enables the goats in the milking competitions to recover from the journey and get into a normal feeding routine before the competition commences. Stripping out, usually around 6 p.m. on the day before the show opens, must be carried out in accordance with the steward's instructions. The judge is likely to inspect the milkers with full udders between 6 a.m. and 7 a.m. the next morning after which the first milking of the test is carried out, the milk weighed and the necessary samples taken. After a pause for breakfast, full judging commences, adults, goatlings and kids appearing in the ring in the order in which the classes appear in the schedule and catalogue. When the class judging is concluded there are often special prizes to be awarded and the exhibitor should make sure that any exhibits eligible should be available if and when wanted. This programme, which may run well into the afternoon, after a break for lunch, is often altered to 'place' the milkers for the award of challenge certificates immediately after the judging of adults is concluded and before the goatlings and kids are called. The programme concludes with the second milking in the milking competition, exactly 24 hours after the competing animals were stripped out.

Making the most of a goat's good points when judging is

A British Alpine Inter-breed and Breed Champion female goat that as a 'first kidder' yielded 12.5 lb. in a 24-hour recognized milking competition and 12 months later 12 lb. in a similar competition without kidding in the intervening period. Owner: H. Hancock. Breeder: the late J. R. Egerton.

taking place is a legitimate exercise provided that the exhibitor complies with the judges' and stewards' instructions. It is done by constant attention to the manner in which the goat is standing. Keep its attention by having a piece of apple or other titbit in your hand: this will be reflected in pricked ears and an alert appearance. A good udder is more prominent, and weak hocks – a common failing – are less noticeable, if the hind feet are well back and wide apart: back the goat a step or two until it assumes the desired posture, which must not appear strained. Maintain strict attention to the task in hand until judging is completed; otherwise the judge may glance back and a moment or two of relaxation on the part of the exhibitor or the goat may reverse a previous decision.

CHAPTER 14

Making a Start

It may seem strange to conclude rather than open this book with advice on how to commence goat-keeping but the basic facts must be understood before a start is even contemplated.

Every prospective goat-keeper should first gain as much information as possible. This can be done by reading the available literature (see p. 108), by visiting owners and inspecting their herds and accommodation, by attending shows, watching the judges at work and the goats being milked, and by talking to exhibitors when the judging is over. Goat-keepers, as a whole, are very willing to share their knowledge and experience.

For general information on goats, join the British Goat Society, which publishes the Herd Book, a Year Book, a monthly Journal and numerous leaflets. The Society will also be able to put you in touch with a local organization where it is possible to make local contacts, and watch demonstrations of hoof trimming, disbudding and other 'operations'. National and regional goat organizations exist in many other countries and a list of these can be found in the Appendix.

The best means of contacting sellers is through the British Goat Society or the nearest local club. Alternatively the leading breeders all advertise in the British Goat Society Year Book, and the monthly Journal contains a limited number of advertisements. Advertisements by the prospective goat-keeper in the 'Wanted' column would certainly bring replies. A visit to a show may present an opportunity of immediate purchase.

When a decision to keep goats has been taken, the preparations, such as providing accommodation, erecting fencing, acquiring foodstuffs and learning to milk, should be made before delivery of stock is taken.

The numbers and ages of goats purchased initially will depend on the aim of the goat-keeper. If the aim is the production of household milk, a start can be made with one or two goatlings in the late autumn after they have been successfully mated. Experience is then gained with feeding and winter management before milk production commences and the impatient wait for the birth of the kids and the production of milk is not unduly prolonged. Goats enjoy company and for that reason it is preferable to start with two rather than one. The quality of foundation stock should be as high as funds will permit: the danger of gaining experience with stock of low quality is the sentimental attachment which may develop and prevent the discarding of this stock subsequently. If there is a desire to exhibit, the purchase of a first-class female kid is a good introduction to the show world.

It is wise, whenever possible, to see a goat before purchase to ensure that the purchaser is not disappointed. Illustrations in this book demonstrate the conformation sought. No goats are perfect, and, by and large, purchasers must expect to get what they pay for. Overseas buyers seeking to purchase from Britain are advised to make a condition of purchase the issue of an Export Certificate. For a comparatively small fee the British Goat Society will arrange for a recognized judge to inspect a goat, which must be earmarked, and a certificate, which also verifies the pedigree, will only be issued if, in the opinion of the judge, the animal is typical of its breed and of sound conformation.

Milk production is dependent, as stated previously, upon the inherited capacity to produce, and upon management. It is possible to make reasonably sure of inherited capacity by purchasing registered pedigree stock the ancestors of which are entitled to bear one or more of the distinguishing marks awarded by the British Goat Society to animals that have milked well in 24-hour milking competitions at shows or in officially recorded lactations. The novice goat-keeper should gain an understanding of these distinguishing marks (see p. 100).

Although the primary objective may be milk production, the purchaser can well decide first on the breed or type preferred and then study milking qualities. The reason for this is that there is little to choose between the milk production of the several breeds: good and inferior milkers, and strains, can be found in all of them.

The price at which goats can be purchased in Britain has always been low in relation to rearing costs, and has not kept pace with inflation. Outstanding prize-winning stock will always command special prices but good second-quality registered pedigree stock, capable of winning lesser prizes can often be obtained at around £10 to £20 for female kids between six and twelve months, £25 to £30 for goatings, and £30 to £40 for milkers. Non-pedigree stock are obtainable at little more than half those prices. Factors, apart from those mentioned above, which generally have a bearing on price are (a) age, (b) whether hornless, disbudded or horned, and (c) the failure of an animal entered in a breed section of the Herd Book to conform to the approved type. An animal entered in the British Section of the Herd Book, other things being equal, is worth less than one entered in one of the breed sections.

Under the British Goat Society's regulations all Members, Associates, and Members of affiliated societies are obliged to register all pedigree stock eligible for registration before sale and to register any Transfer of Ownership effected. A condition of purchase of a pedigree goat should be that the seller will deliver with the animal the appropriate registration card with the transfer of ownership, acknowledging the purchaser as the registered owner, endorsed thereon by the Society.

If the goat is ear-marked its identity can be checked by reference to the Society.

APPENDIX

BRIEF EXPLANATION OF DISTINGUISHING MARKS AWARDED BY THE BRITISH GOAT SOCIETY

CHAMPION — A prefix awarded when a female goat that has kidded, or a male goat over one year old, has won, under three different judges, a specified number of Inspection Certificates, open to inter-breed competition, for Best in Show and, additionally, in the case of a female, Certificates awarded on the basis of inspection and of points awarded in the 24-hour milking competition and has qualified for a Q* (see below).

BREED CHAMPION — An affix awarded when a female goat that has kidded or a male goat over one year old has won, under three different judges, a specified number of Inspection Certificates for Best of Breed in Show and additionally, in the case of a female, has qualified for a * (see below).

Q* — An affix awarded when a female goat has obtained a minimum of 20 points in a 24-hour recognized milking competition, in which points are allotted for milk yield, butter-fat percentage and days since last kidding, and the butter-fat percentage at each milking is not less than 4 per cent.

* — An affix awarded to a female goat that has obtained a minimum of 18 points in a similar competition and the butter-fat percentage is not less than 3.25 per cent at each milking.

N.B. The basis for the award of points in 24-hour recognized milking competitions is:

For each 1 lb. of milk – 1 point (and pro rata)
For each complete 10 days since last kidding one tenth of a point (with a maximum of 3.6 points)
For each ¼ lb. of butter fat – 5 points (and pro rata)
In a few competitions, points are allotted also for 'other solids' on a basis of 1 point for each ¼ lb. (and pro rata) and an additional 2 points have then to be obtained to qualify for the affix.
A yield of less than 5½ lb. in the 24 hours or less than 3 per cent butter fat at each milking disqualifies, and the goat must have kidded at least ten days and not more than two years before the competition.
When a goat qualifies for either of the above two awards and its dam and further ancestors in the direct female line have qualified for either of the awards, a numeral follows the Q* or * to indicate the number of such ancestors, without a break, that have so qualified.

R — A prefix awarded when a female goat is officially milk recorded and has yielded a minimum of 2,000 lb. of milk in a lactation period of not more than 365 days. Two numerals follow the letter R and indicate the maximum yield in thousands and hundreds of lb. e.g. R38 indicates 3800 lb.

RM — A prefix awarded when a goat is registered in the Register of Merit for which the goat itself and its dam must both have qualified for the prefix R29 or higher.

AR — A prefix awarded when a goat is entered in the Advanced Register for which the goat itself must have qualified for the R35 or higher award with an average butter-fat percentage or not less than 3.5 per cent. Its dam must be in the Advanced Register of Merit and the goat's sire must be out of a goat so registered.

† — A prefix awarded to a male goat whose dam and sire's dam are both entitled to the affix Q* or *.

§ — A prefix awarded to a male goat whose dam and sire's dam are both entitled to the R prefix, followed by numerals indicating the maximum yields in thousands and hundreds of lb. that the said dam and sire's dam have produced e.g. §34/42 (see R prefix).

§§ — A prefix awarded to a male goat whose dam and sire's dam are entitled to the RM or AR prefix, and whose sire is entitled to the § or § §, followed by numerals as awarded with the RM and the AR.

SR — A prefix awarded to a male goat that has sired a minimum of five goats that have qualified for the Q*, *, or R.

THE BRITISH GOAT SOCIETY

Mrs. S. May, Lion House, Rougham, Bury St. Edmunds, Suffolk

AFFILIATED SOCIETIES

ANGLO NUBIAN BREED SOCIETY

Hon. Secretary, Miss N. Wing, Hall Farm Cottage, Hooton Lane, Ravenfield, Rotherham, S65 4NH.

BINGLEY & DISTRICT GOAT CLUB

Hon. Secretary, Mrs. D. Wright, Bay of Biscay Farm, Haworth Road, Allerton, Bradford.

BUCKINGHAMSHIRE GOAT SOCIETY

Hon. Secretary, Mr. Nicholson, North Park Lodge, Chequers Estate, Butlers Cross, Aylesbury, Bucks.

CAMBRIDGESHIRE GOAT CLUB

Hon. Secretary, R. M. Marsters, Decreke Farm, Beck Row Common, Bury St. Edmunds, Suffolk.

CHESHIRE DAIRY GOAT SOCIETY

Hon. Secretary, Mrs. M. Killick, The Oaks, Warmingham, Sandbach, Cheshire.

COLCHESTER, SUDBURY & DISTRICT GOAT CLUB

Hon. Secretary, Miss P. V. Minter, "The Chestnuts", Ipswich Road, Ardleigh, Colchester, Essex.

CORNWALL DAIRY GOATKEEPERS' ASSOCIATION

Hon. Secretary, Mrs. E. Morris, Marroy, Toldish, Indian Queens, St. Columb, Cornwall TR9 6HL.

THE DERBYSHIRE GOAT CLUB

Hon. Secretary, Mrs. M. M. Hollis, Stonecroft, Chesterfield Road, Duckmanton, Nr. Chesterfield, Derbys.

DEVON GOAT SOCIETY

Hon. Secretary, Mrs. Russell Welch, Skindles Farm, Harbertonford, Totnes, Devon TQ9 7HT.

DURHAM DAIRY GOAT SOCIETY

Hon. Secretary, J. T. Walton, 69 Hardie Drive, West Boldon, Co. Durham.

ENGLISH GOLDEN GUERNSEY GOAT CLUB

Hon. Secretary, Mrs. K. Roberts, Henstead Lodge, Needham, Harleston, Norfolk.

HAMPSHIRE GOAT CLUB

Hon. Secretary, Miss M. E. K. Pennington, Browns, 52 Broad Street, Alresford, Hants. SO24 9AN.

HULL & EAST RIDING GOAT SOCIETY

Hon. Secretary, Miss H. Cowling, The Vicarage, Garton-on-the-Wold, Driffield, Yorks.

IPSWICH & DISTRICT GOAT CLUB

Hon. Secretary, P. Cox, Hawkdene, Hadleigh Road, Elmsett, Ipswich.

KENT GOAT CLUB

Hon. Secretary, Mrs. B. Taylor, Little Shuttlesfield Farm, Acrise, Folkestone, Kent.

LANCASHIRE DAIRY GOAT SOCIETY

Secretary, J. B. Turner, 14 Bradley Lane, Wigan, Lancs.

LINCOLNSHIRE GOAT SOCIETY

Hon. Secretary, Mrs. V. Wilmot, Happylands Farm, Owersby Moor, Market Rasen, Lincs. LN8 3YN.

MANX DAIRY GOAT SOCIETY

Hon. Secretary, Brielle, St. Marks, Isle of Man.

MID ESSEX GOAT CLUB

Hon. Secretary, Mrs. and Miss Trigg, The Anchorage, Nathans Lane, Writtle, Nr. Chelmsford, Essex.

NORFOLK & SUFFOLK GOAT SOCIETY

Hon. Secretary, Miss C. Loveridge, "Sandylands", Waxham, Sea Palling, Norfolk.

NORTHANTS & DISTRICT GOAT SOCIETY

Secretary, Mrs. B. Ford, Chapel Farm, Ashton, Oundle, Peterborough PE8 5LD.

NORTHERN ENGLAND GOAT CLUB

Hon. Secretary, Mrs. Laing, Twislehope Hermitage, Hawick, Roxburgh, Scotland.

NORTHERN IRELAND GOAT CLUB

Hon. Secretary, Miss E. Barbara Gibbins, Finlarig, Burren, Ballynahinch, Co. Down, N. Ireland.

NORTH STAFFORDSHIRE GOAT CLUB

Hon. Secretary, Mrs. B. White, Fairview Farm, Thorny Edge, Bagnall, Stoke-on-Trent, Staffs.

NORTH WALES GOAT SOCIETY

Hon. Sec., Mrs. Harris, Clogwyn Guto, Deiniolen, Caerns.

NORWICH & DISTRICT GOAT CLUB

Hon. Secretary, Mrs. D. Sayer, Breck Farm, Weybourne Holt, Norfolk.

NOTTINGHAMSHIRE GOAT CLUB

Hon. Secretary, Mr. C. B. Marrison, 8 Sheppards Row, Queen Street, Southwell, Notts.

PENNINE GOAT CLUB

Hon. Secretary, Mrs. H. Varley, Gate House, Old Mount Road, Marsden, Nr. Huddersfield, Yorks.

PONTEFRACT & DISTRICT GOAT CLUB

Hon. Secretary, Mrs. M. J. Rogers, Whitgift Hall, Whitgift, Nr. Goole, Yorks.

SCOTTISH GOATKEEPERS' FEDERATION

Hon. Secretary, Mrs. M. Forrest, Mount Vernon Nursery, Glasgow E2.

SHROPSHIRE & HEREFORDSHIRE GOAT CLUB

Hon. Secretary, Mrs. J. Winter, Farmhouse, Leinthall Starkes, Ludlow, Salop. SY8 2HP.

SOMERSET & WILTSHIRE GOAT SOCIETY

Hon. Secretary, Miss J. Gordon Macleod, Chestnut Tree Cottage, Doynton, Bristol BS15 5TA.

SURREY GOAT CLUB

Hon. Secretary, Mrs. H. Hanbury, Foxbury, The Ridge, Woldingham, Surrey.

SUSSEX COUNTY GOAT CLUB

Hon. Secretary, Mrs. Paris, Willow Cottage, East Chiltington, Nr. Lewes, Sussex.

SWAFFHAM & DISTRICT GOAT CLUB

Hon. Secretary, Mrs. J. Baxter, Lime Kiln Farm, Lynn Road, Swaffham, Norfolk.

TYNESIDE DAIRY GOAT SOCIETY

Misses E. & J. D. Bolam, Holeyn Hall, Wylam, Northumberland.

WARWICKSHIRE GOAT SOCIETY

Hon. Secretary, Mrs. R. Ragg, Foxcote Farm House, Shipston-on-Stour, Warwickshire.

WAVENEY VALLEY GOAT CLUB

Hon. Secretary, Mrs. P. Carter, Blue Tile Farm, Brampton, Beccles, Suffolk.

WELSH & MARCHES GOAT SOCIETY

Hon. Secretary, Mrs. M. Hughes, Hand Farm House, Hand Farm Road, Pontypool, Mons. NP4 5RD.

WESSEX GOAT CLUB

Hon. Secretary, Mrs. J. Ballam, Eastwood, Danes Hill, Dalwood, Nr. Axminster, Devon EX13 7HH.

WORCESTERSHIRE GOAT SOCIETY

Hon. Secretary, Mrs. C. M. Wickett, The Orchards, Harvington, Nr. Evesham, Worcs.

YORKSHIRE GOAT SOCIETY

Hon. Secretary, Mrs. Harben Williams, Field House, Gomersal, Cleckheaton, Yorks.

OVERSEAS ASSOCIATIONS

Changes of address take place from time to time: if a communication sent to any of the following associations does not elicit a reply, contact the Ministry of Agriculture of the country concerned.

AUSTRALIA

Goat Breeders' Society of Australia, Box 4317 G.P.O., Sydney 2001, New South Wales, Australia.

BELGIUM

Fédération Nationale des Éleveurs de Chèvres et de Moutons Laitiers, Blvd. de Jodoigne 64, Louvain, Belgium.

CANADA

Canadian Goat Society, R.R.I., Ormstown, Quebec, Canada.

DENMARK

Associated Danish Goat Breeders Association, Svanninge, Millinge, Denmark.

FRANCE

Fédération Nationale des Éleveurs de Chèvres, 36 rue Fontaine, Paris 9e., France.

GERMANY

Arbeitsgemeinschaft der Landesverbände deutscher Ziegenzüchter e.V., Walkmüllstr. 63a, 62 Wiesbaden, W. Germany.

ISRAEL

Goat Breeders Association, Hadar-Ramatayim, P.O.B. 25.

JAPAN

Japan Goat Registration Association, 1-50 Yushima-Tenjincho, Bunkyo-ku, Tokyo, Japan.

MALTA

Department of Agriculture, Valetta, Malta.

NETHERLANDS

Nederlandse Organisatie voor de Geitenfokkerij, Altingstraat 189, The Hague, Holland.

NEW ZEALAND

N.Z. Dairy Goat Association, Inc., Papanui, R.D.Z., Kumeu, Auckland, New Zealand.

N.Z. Goat Association, 6 Tuhimata St., Auckland, E1.

N.Z. Goat Breeders' Association, "Hope Farm", Simpson Road, Ranui, Auckland 8.

NORWAY

Norwegian Sheep and Goat Association, Parkvein 71, Oslo.

SPAIN

Associación General de Ganaderos, Madrid, Spain.

SWEDEN

Svenska getavelsföreningen, Kristianstad, Sweden.

SWITZERLAND

Schweiz. Ziegenzüchterverband Geschäftstelle, Herr R. Kanzi-Kaufmann, Seestrasse 345, 8035 Zurich, Switzerland.

TRINIDAD

Trinidad Goat Society, 64 Sixth Avenue, Barataria, Trinidad.

UNION OF SOUTH AFRICA

Boer Goat Breeders' Society, Roodekrantz, Somerset East, South West Africa.

South African Milch Goat Breeders Association, 17 Vermuelen St., De Aar, Cape Province, South West Africa.

South African Mohair Growers Association, P.O.B. 50, Jansenville, South West Africa.

UNITED STATES OF AMERICA

American Dairy Goat Association, P.O.B. 186, Spindale, North Carolina, U.S.A.

American Goat Society Inc., C.W. Romer, 7900 East 66 St., Kansas City, U.S.A.

American Angora Goat Breeders' Association, P.O.B. 409, Rocksprings, Texas, U.S.A.

FURTHER READING

Breeds of Goats, British Goat Society.

Common Ailments of the Dairy Goat, British Goat Society.

Dairy Work for Goat-Keepers, British Goat Society.

Goat Husbandry, D. Mackenzie, Faber & Faber Ltd.

Goat-Keeping, British Goat Society.

Goat Production in the Tropics, C. Devendra & Marca Burns.

MAGAZINES AND PERIODICALS

The Monthly Journal, British Goat Society.

The Year Book, British Goat Society.

The Herd Book, (annual parts), British Goat Society.

The above periodicals are free to members of the British Goat Society.

MISCELLANEOUS

The British Goat Society also publishes a number of Leaflets on various subjects related to goat-keeping, Herd Registers, Milk Recording Books, Service Certificates Books etc.

INDEX